Microprocessor Appreciation
Level III

Units in this series

Microelectronic Systems	Level I
Microelectronic Systems	Level II
Microelectronic Systems	Level III
Microprocessor-based Systems	Level IV
Microprocessor-based Systems	Level V
Microprocessor Appreciation	Level III
Microprocessor Principles	Level IV

Microprocessor Appreciation

Level III

Glyn Martin

Open University

TECHNICIAN EDUCATION COUNCIL
in association with
HUTCHINSON
London Melbourne Sydney Auckland Johannesburg

Hutchinson & Co. (Publishers) Ltd

An imprint of the Hutchinson Publishing Group

17–21 Conway Street, London W1P 6JD

Hutchinson Group (Australia) Pty Ltd
30–32 Cremorne Street, Richmond South, Victoria 3121
PO Box 151, Broadway, New South Wales 2007

Hutchinson Group (NZ) Ltd
32–34 View Road, PO Box 40–086, Glenfield, Auckland 10

Hutchinson Group (SA) (Pty) Ltd
PO Box 337, Bergvlei 2012, South Africa

First published 1982

© Technician Education Council 1982

Set in Times

Printed in Great Britain by The Anchor Press Ltd
and bound by Wm Brendon & Son Ltd
both of Tiptree, Essex

British Library Cataloguing in Publication Data
Microprocessor appreciation.
  3
. 1. Microprocessors
  I. Technician Education Council
  621.3819′5835   TK7895.M5

ISBN 0 09 146821 3

Contents

Preface   9
Introduction   11

1   How a microprocessor controls a system   13
   1.1   What is a microprocessor?   13
   1.2   Controlling a system with a microcomputer   15
   1.3   How the microprocessor handles information   16
   1.4   Summary   18
   Questions   19

2   What is in a microprocessor?   20
   2.1   Technological advances   20
   2.2   The microcomputer system   22
   2.3   Information transfer   26
   2.4   Summary   26
   Questions   26

3   Peripheral devices   28
   3.1   The keyboard   29
   3.2   Paper-tape reader and punch   30
   3.3   Printer   31
   3.4   Visual display unit   32
   3.5   Backing stores   33
   3.6   Using transducers   33
   3.7   Summary   34
   Questions   35

4   A microprocessor controlling a system   36
   4.1   System task description   36
   4.2   The signals within the system   37
   4.3   Polling the input transducers   38
   4.4   Summary   39
   Questions   40

5   The use of interrupts in a microcomputer controller   41
   5.1   A more complex temperature control system   41
   5.2   On receipt of an interrupt   42
   5.3   Interrupt-handling segment for the temperature
       controller   42

5.4   Systems with more than one interface device
        allowed to interrupt   43
5.5   Polling versus interrupts   44
5.6   Summary   44
Questions   44

6   Maintenace of microprocessor-based systems   45
6.1   Hardware or software fault?   45
6.2   Maintenance aids   46
6.3   Summary   47
Questions   47

7   Microprocessor programming   48
7.1   Microcomputer programming   48
7.2   Assembler programming   49
7.3   Data representation   51
7.4   High-level language programming   53
7.5   Summary   54
Questions   54

8   A register model of a microprocessor   56
8.1   The model   56
8.2   Models for other microprocessors   59
8.3   Microprocessor instructions   59
8.4   Summary   61
Questions   62

9   Assembler programming   64
9.1   The form of assembler statements   64
9.2   Assembler programming examples   64
9.3   Assembler instructions in more detail   65
9.4   Program loops   71
9.5   Input and output instructions   72
9.6   Subroutine calls   74
9.7   Discussion   76
9.8   Summary   76
Questions   77

10   **Programming example**   78
10.1   Specification of the temperature and display system   78
10.2   System elements to be used   79
10.3   Flow diagram for the program   83
10.4   The program segments   83
10.5   The complete program   91
10.6   Discussion   92
10.7   Summary   92
Questions   93

Appendix: Instruction summary   97

Answers to Questions   103

Index   110

Preface

This book is one of a series on microelectronics/microprocessors published by Hutchinson on behalf of the Technician Education Council. The books in the series are designed for use with units associated with Technician Education Council programmes.

In June 1978 the United Kingdom Prime Minister expressed anxiety about the effect to be expected from the introduction of micro-processors on the pattern of employment in specific industries. From this stemmed an initiative through the Department of Industry and the National Enterprise Board to encourage the use and development of microprocessor technology.

An important aspect of such a development programme was seen as being the education and training of personnel for both the research, development and manufacture of microelectronics material and equipment, and the application of these in other industries. In 1979 a project was established by the Technician Education Council for the development of technician education programme units (a unit is a specification of the objectives to be attained by a student) and associated learning packages, this project being funded by the Department of Industry and managed on their behalf by the National Computing Centre Ltd.

TEC established a committee involving industry, both as producers and users of microelectronics, and educationists. In addition wide-spread consultations took place. Programme units were developed for technicians and technician engineers concerned with the design, manufacture and servicing aspects incorporating microelectronic devices. Five units were produced:

Microelectronic Systems	Level I
Microelectronic Systems	Level II
Microelectronic Systems	Level III
Microprocessor-based Systems	Level IV
Microprocessor-based Systems	Level V

Units were also produced for those technicians who required a general understanding of the range of applications of microelectronic devices and their potential:

Microprocessor Appreciation	Level III
Microprocessor Principles	Level IV

This phase was then followed by the development of the learning packages, involving three writing teams, the key people in these teams being:

Microelectronic Systems I, II, III —   P. Cooke
Microprocessor-based Systems IV —   A. Potton
Microprocessor-based Systems V —   M. J. Morse
Microprocessor Appreciation III —   G. Martin
Microprocessor Principles IV   —   G. Martin

The project director during the unit specification stage was N. Bonnett, assisted by R. Bertie. Mr Bonnett continued as consultant during the writing stage. The project manager was W. Bolton, assisted by K. Snape.

Self-learning

As an aid to self-learning, questions are included in every chapter. These appear at the end of the chapters with references in the margin of the chapter text (for example, Q1.2), indicating the most appropriate position for self-learning use. Answers to each question are given at the back of the book.

The books in this series have therefore been developed for use in either the classroom teaching situation or for self-learning.

Introduction

This book is intended as an introduction to the potential applications of microprocessors for students whose main line of study is not electronics. As such my overall concern when writing the book was to indicate the potential of microprocessors to a sufficient depth to provide a basic background knowledge for technicians in modern industry. This book is written to the objectives specified in the TEC Unit Microprocessor Appreciation U79/640. No previous knowledge of microprocessors is assumed.

It is not the aim of this book to produce fully competent microprocessor programmers, but rather to explain the process of program development so that students may appreciate the potential of microprocessors in modern industry. My teaching strategy is therefore to avoid the details of microprocessor architecture and programming techniques so that a student may realise that the underlying nature of microprocessors is governed by relatively simple ideas. Hopefully, a student can, by reading this book, move from a complete lack of knowledge of microprocessors to a stage where they have the confidence to feel able to program a microprocessor to perform a relatively simple task. The practical example at the end of the book is central to this last process.

The practical system described in Chapter 10 uses the ideas introduced in the earlier chapters to show that a microprocessor can, using only a few simple instructions, be programmed to perform a non-trivial task. Before the advent of microprocessors this task would have required a considerable amount of experienced design effort.

Acknowledgements

I thank two of my Open University colleagues, Cheryl Hitchcock for her help with the early drafts of Chapters 1–3 and Nick Heap for his critical reading of the manuscript. My thanks go also to Christine Martindale who organised the efficient typing and preparation of the manuscript.

GLYN MARTIN

Chapter 1 How a microprocessor controls a system

Objectives of this chapter *When you have completed studying this chapter you should be able to:*

1 *Understand how and why a microprocessor can be used to control a system.*
2 *Understand how a series of instructions can change the state of the microprocessor.*
3 *Be able to use binary notation.*

Microprocessors have been widely talked about recently as components that can do almost anything! Although this is a gross exaggeration of their potential, microprocessors can be used in many new applications where large computers would be totally inapplicable.

1.1 What is a microprocessor?

The *microprocessor* with other parts around it forms a small computer known as a *microcomputer*. These machines are similar in operation to the standard *mainframe* computers that have been around for many years, but because microcomputers are smaller and cheaper, they can be used in new applications.

Figure 1.1 shows a mainframe computer and Figure 1.2 a microcomputer for comparison.

In the early years of computing, computers were so expensive that they were used only in large institutions by highly skilled staff. In these cases, one computer would be used for many different tasks, e.g. handling records and salaries in banks or solving complex scientific problems.

As yet, microcomputers cannot replace mainframe computers in tasks involving very large numbers of calculations. They can, however, solve similar problems which deal with smaller quantities of numbers. Because of their low cost, small size and reliability, microcomputers can be used in new applications where a mainframe computer would be inappropriate. A microcomputer can be used to control a few simple tasks, for instance, controlling traffic lights or the cycles of a washing machine. Such tasks need not use the micro-

Figure 1.1   A mainframe computer – the ICL 2900 (*Courtesy: ICL Ltd*)

Figure 1.2   A microcomputer – the Commodore PET (*Courtesy: Commodore*)

computer's full capacity, but could still prove cheaper and more reliable than the components it replaced. Because the microcomputer is so small, it can be used in places where a large mainframe computer, because of its size, could not be used, e.g. controlling the wing flaps in an aircraft.

Q1.1

1.2 Controlling a system with a microcomputer

To demonstrate the ways in which a microcomputer can control a system, I will use a simple application as an example. Imagine a warehouse for motor car parts. The stock areas have different bins containing different components. A central microcomputer is used to keep track of the numbers of parts in stock, to indicate when stocks are getting low and to monitor stock flow so that popular items can be ordered in larger quantities.

When a particular part is required, a worker on the warehouse floor takes the part from the appropriate bin and presses a button on the bin to indicate its removal. The microcomputer notes all the different button presses and processes the information in a variety of ways. The complete system is shown in diagrammatical form in Figure 1.3. As the figure shows, the microcomputer is also connected to a TV-type screen, a keyboard and a printer. An operator can key in certain

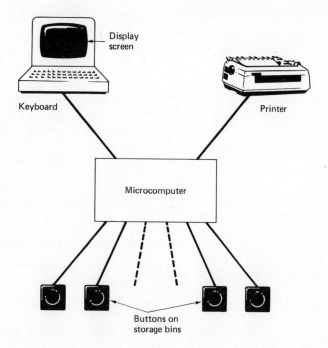

Figure 1.3 Block diagram of a microprocessor-based stock control system

commands for information. This will appear on the screen or be printed out for a permanent record. The microcomputer could give the user a variety of information such as:

- a list of parts sold that day
- the number of a specific part sold in a day
- the total cost of parts sold in a day
- a list of the numbers of parts remaining

To perform such tasks, the microcomputer must have certain information available. It must be able to:

- keep track of the time
- know the cost of each part
- know when a part is removed
- respond to key presses on the keyboard

To be able to process the information in a meaningful way, the micro-computer must have a description of the tasks it is to perform. This description is known as the *software* and is in the form of a computer *program* which is built into the microprocessor. The microcomputer and all the other physical components are known as the *hardware*.

When a button is pressed to indicate the removal of a part, the micro-computer will add one to the correct total. This total must then be stored somewhere. The microcomputer does this is an electronic memory sometimes known as the *data store*. It is this form of *memory*, therefore, that holds information like the cost of parts and numbers of parts sold. The microprocessor can then call on this information at any time and process it in the required manner. The task (in this case to add 1 to the number of parts sold and place the total in the data store) can be expressed as a series of operations called *instructions* to be performed by the processor. This sequence of instructions is known as a *program*. It is just one of the lists of instructions which the microcomputer can use, and is part of the software.

The software or programs are held in another sort of memory known as the *program store*. So the program and the data which the micro-processor will use to perform a task are both stored in separate memories until required by the microprocessor.

Q1.2

1.3   How the microprocessor handles information

First let us look at the way the microprocessor receives information. I have said that the microprocessor detects the pressing of a button at a stock bin and thus counts the removed stock. To do this the micro-processor is connected via a wire link to the button and its associated electronic circuitry on the stock bin. When the button is pressed, the voltage on the wire connected to the microprocessor is changed. This gives two distinct voltage levels: one when the button is at rest and another when it is depressed. It is common to represent these levels by the symbols 0 (zero) and 1 (one). Usually the low voltage is represented by a zero and the high voltage by a one. The microprocessor is able to detect the two different voltage levels. Indeed, the entire internal operation of the microprocessor is based on detecting differences of this type. Information received in discrete levels like this is known as *binary* information.

Q1.3 Part of the microprocessor's task in the example is to store the total number of articles removed from stock, but as the microprocessor can only recognise voltages of two levels, the numbers must be coded in terms of ones and zeros. *Binary notation* is the name used for this code.

Binary representation

In a binary counting code, only two digits, 0 and 1, are used, whereas in our normal denary counting system we use ten digits, 0 to 9. Each extra digit in binary stands for an increased power of 2 as is shown in Table 1.1.

Table 1.1

Denary number	Denary value of each binary digit							
	128 (2^7)	64 (2^6)	32 (2^5)	16 (2^4)	8 (2^3)	4 (2^2)	2 (2^1)	1 (2^0)
1								1
2							1	0
5						1	0	1
27				1	1	0	1	1
151	1	0	0	1	0	1	1	1

To convert from a denary to a binary number all you have to do is express the denary number as the sum of powers of 2. For example, the number 27 is

$$16(2^4) + 8(2^3) + 2(2^1) + 1(2^0)$$

The binary code is formed by using ones for these powers and zeros for the other missing powers. Therefore 27 in binary is 11011.

To convert from binary to denary all you have to do is add the power of 2 indicated by the presence of ones in the number. For example

$$10011 = 16(2^4) + 2(2^1) + 1(2^0)$$
$$= 19$$

In the binary code used by the microprocessor, groups of eight binary digits can often be used to represent denary numbers as follows:

00000001	represents denary 1
00000010	represents denary 2
00000100	represents denary 4
⋮	⋮ ⋮
11010100	represents denary $128 + 64 + 16 + 4 = 212$

Each one of the binary digits is called a *bit* and the group of bits a *word*. Some sizes of word are used more commonly than others and have therefore been given special names. For example, an 8-bit word is called a *byte*. The largest number that can be represented in the 8-bit word is 11111111 or 255 in denary. A microprocessor may use **Q1.4, 1.5** two or more of these words to represent larger numbers.

Binary programs

All instructions handled by the microprocessor are also in this type of binary code. Binary representation of instructions is known as *machine code*. As I will show later, it is very time-consuming and error-prone to write instructions in this form. Therefore it is common for microprocessor programs to be written in *assembly language* where *mnemonic instruction* codes and names refer directly to binary equivalents. Before the microprocessor can handle such instructions, the assembly code must be converted to machine code. This task is performed by a special computer program known as an *assembler*.

Assembly code and machine code are known as *low-level languages* as they are closely related to machine operations and can be translated into binary instructions. Some microcomputers have programs available to them that will translate *high-level languages* into machine code. These languages, such as BASIC, FORTRAN, FORTH, PASCAL and COBOL, are more closely related to written English. High-level languages tend to be used on general-purpose microcomputers where new programs are often put into the machine. They are generally inappropriate for other products based on microprocessors where the same tasks are repeated using the same **Q1.6, 1.7** program.

I will be returning to the topic of microprocessor programming in Chapter 7.

1.4   Summary

1   A microcomputer is similar to conventional mainframe computers but can be used in new applications because it is small and cheap.

2   The microcomputer and the devices associated with it in a particular application are known as the hardware of a system.

3   The series of instructions which control the processor is known as a program and is called the software of the system.

4   A binary code system is used to represent numbers and instructions within the microcomputer.

5   The basic rules for representing ordinary (denary numbers) by binary can be summarised by the following for a 4-digit binary code:

$$1 \quad 1 \quad 1 \quad 0$$
$$(1 \times 2^3) + (1 \times 2^2) + (1 \times 2^1) + (0 \times 2^0)$$
$$(1 \times 8) + (1 \times 4) + (1 \times 2) + (0 \times 1)$$
14 (denary)

6   Each of the binary digits is called a bit.

7   Many microprocessors handle data and instructions eight bits at a time.

8   Programming the microcomputer directly with patterns of ones and zeros is called machine coding.

Questions

1.1   What are the three main reasons that have led to microcomputers being used in new applications?

1.2   *(a)*   What is the software of the microcomputer?
(b)   What is the hardware of the microcomputer?

1.3   What sort of information is stored in the memory of a microcomputer system?

1.4   What are the following binary numbers in denary?
(a)   1101
(b)   0010
(c)   11111110
(d)   01010101

1.5   What are the following denary numbers in 8-bit binary *code*?
(a)   49
(b)   139
(c)   255

1.6   Give an example of:
(a)   a low-level language
(b)   a high-level language

1.7   How does the microcomputer convert assembly language into the machine code?

Chapter 2 What is in a microprocessor?

Objectives of this chapter *When you have completed studying this chapter you should be able to:*

1 *Draw a block diagram of a generalised microcomputer and understand the functions of its component parts.*
2 *Understand the difference between the terms RAM, ROM, PROM and EPROM.*
3 *Explain how information is transferred within the microcomputer.*

As I explained in the previous chapter, the microprocessor with other devices around it forms the basis of a microcomputer which is very similar in operation to a standard mainframe computer. In this chapter I aim to explain how advances in technology have enabled computers of this size to be built, what devices they contain and how the 'inside' of a microcomputer is organised.

2.1 Technological advances

The development of the microprocessor can be seen as a merging of the advances in electronic devices and computer technology. Any computer is made up of thousands of electronic devices and connections. The main building block of a microprocessor circuit is the transistor and these devices are the basis of the on/off, 1/0 binary logic that enables the microprocessor to function. In the late 1950s transistors were used as separate devices and a radio or television from that era might contain from six to sixteen separate transistors. Advances in manufacturing techniques enabled several transistors to be connected together onto one small wafer of silicon to form a complete circuit, known as an integrated circuit. Recently, such circuits have become known as 'silicon chips' as they are made of small flakes of silicon which are usually less than 1 cm square. That shown in Figure 2.1 is actually only 5 mm across.

Each chip or integrated circuit is then packed in a plastic casing to protect it and to provide manageable connection pins to the outside world. The resulting device is about 5.3 cm long and an example can be seen in Figure 2.2.

By looking at the way in which the number of transistors in an integrated circuit has varied with time (see Figure 2.3), we can get a

Figure 2.1 A single chip microcomputer – the 8748. Actual size is about 5 mm across. *(Courtesy: The Open University)*

Figure 2.2 An example of a packaged microprocessor

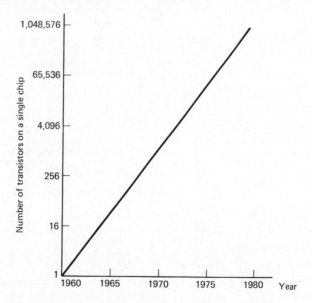

Figure 2.3 The increase in the number of transistors on a single chip

good measure of the way this technology has advanced over the last twenty years.

Devices with more than 100 transistors per chip became known as LSI chips (Large Scale Integration) and, by 1975, chips were available with over 60,000 devices on one integrated circuit. The number of transistor-like devices that it is possible to put on each chip is now approximately doubling every other year.

One of the first integrated circuits designed to act as a microprocessor was developed by Intel in 1971. Since then improvements in manufac-turing technology mean that more components of a computer can be made on the same 'chip' and now complete microcomputers are available on a single integrated circuit.

2.2   The microcomputer system

Q2.1

The components of a general microcomputer system are shown in Figure 2.4. The system consists of the microprocessor unit, memory sections and a section for inputs and outputs.

The central processing unit (CPU)

In most microcomputers the microprocessor forms the *central processing unit* (CPU) for the computer. This unit initiates all actions within the computer and controls some of them. The CPU can temporarily store instructions that it has read from the computer's memory. These instructions are in the form of strings of binary digits or bits. The number of bits stored together in this way is known as the *word* length of the microprocessor. Eight-bit words or bytes (such as 11001010) are used in most microprocessors.

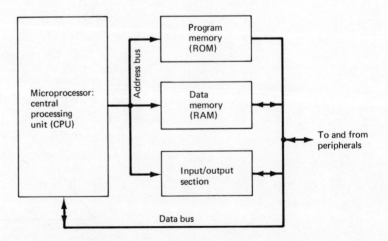

Figure 2.4   Block diagram of a typical microcomputer system

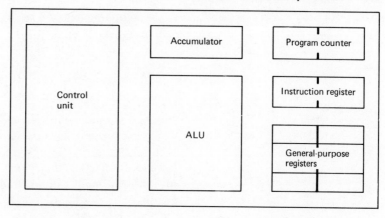

Figure 2.5 Block diagram of the inside of a microprocessor (CPU)

Whilst words are in the CPU they are stored in special locations called *registers*. These are rather like labelled pigeon holes since each register has a name and is capable of storing information in the form of binary words. The CPU has several types of storage register and these are used for different purposes.

Figure 2.5 shows a block diagram of a CPU. As information reaches it, the CPU separates the instructions from the data and routes them to different registers. A special register called the *program counter* keeps a record of the location in the computer's memory of the next instruction which the CPU is going to process. The CPU processes the instruction by *fetching* it from that location and performing the tasks specified by the instruction. This is called *executing* the instruction.

Because the CPU works in this sequential fashion it needs its operations to occur at the correct time. Therefore the CPU needs to be supplied with an electrical signal from a crystal-controlled clock. The speed of this clock controls the speed of operation of the processor. Often this clock will have a frequency of several megahertz.

Another crucial part of the CPU is the *arithmetic and logical unit* (ALU). This portion of the computer, as its name implies, performs all arithmetic and logical functions. It operates on all the data passing through the CPU by adding or subtracting binary words or performing logical operations on them. The ALU usually has no storage registers of its own, but uses others within the CPU. The register most frequently used is known as the *accumulator*. The ALU can receive a word from the accumulator, process it and return the resulting word to the accumulator.

Q2.2, 2.3

Memories

The information processed in the CPU is received from and returned to the computer memory. As I stated before, this information can be split into two types: the instructions to the CPU (or the program) and data. The data can consist of both non-processed information as it is received by the computer and processed information ready to send out of the computer. All this information is in the form of binary words and is stored in a variety of memory devices.

In a microcomputer, the memory is usually an electronic system which can be thought of as a series of separate *locations* all identical to each other and which can store different patterns of ones and zeros. Each location has a unique binary name known as the *address* of that location. Normally one word of binary digits can be stored in each location. As mentioned before, many microprocessors use a word length of 8 bits or 1 byte. To gain access to a word of information stored in the memory, the address specifying that word's location is presented to the electrical connections to the memory device and the memory responds by supplying the value or information held in that location to the CPU. When a word is taken out of a location in this way, it is referred to as *reading* a location. When a word is put in a memory location, the address specifying the word's destination is sent to the memory device and then the information is supplied to the memory location by the CPU. This is known as *writing* to a location.

There are two distinct types of memory to cope with these processes. With one memory type, known as the *read only memory* or *ROM*, words can only be *read from* the locations by the microprocessor. No words can be written into the memory whilst the memory chip is installed in the computer. ROMs are usually used to store the program, which consists of a series of instructions, because this does not change during use.

With other memory types, binary words can be both read from and written to the memory locations by the microprocessor. These memories are known as read/write memories or more commonly *random access memories* or *RAMs*. RAMs are mainly used for storing binary data which changes during the operation of a program. As I said above, ROMs cannot be written to by the microprocessor once they are installed in the computer, so most ROMs are programmed with the required contents during the manufacturing of the integrated circuit. However there are some types of ROM that can be programmed after the integrated circuit has been made. These are given a special name and are known as *programmable read only memories (PROMs)*. These are useful devices in that they can be programmed by the customer.

Because the programming can be carried out on site by the customer, these ROM chips are sometimes known as *field programmable ROMs (FPROMs)*. The FPROM is usually programmed by a portable machine called a PROM programmer (see Figure 2.6), which works

Figure 2.6 A PROM programmer *(Courtesy: The Open University)*

by supplying a voltage to 'blow' selected electronic circuits rather like fuses specially built into the PROM. If a fuse is blown, it is logically interpreted as a zero, and as a one if the fuse is intact. In this way, the programmer can specify the pattern or program to be 'blown' by the PROM programmer.

However, like the manufactured ROMs, once they are programmed, PROM programs cannot be changed. As it is expensive and inconvenient to change a program by reordering ROMs from an integrated circuit manufacturer, another type of memory is used for development work. These are known as *erasable PROMs (EPROMs)* and can be both programmed and reprogrammed.

A typical EPROM (see Figure 2.7) contains a series of small electronic circuits called cells with groups of electrons trapped into them. To produce the pattern needed for the program, the cells are either left empty or charged with electrons by applying the correct voltages to the integrated circuit connection pins. Often, a PROM programmer can also be used to perform this task.

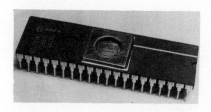

Figure 2.7 An ultra-violet erasable EPROM

Usually the program in an EPROM is erased by shining ultra-violet light through a quartz window on the top of the device. This causes the electrons to drift out of the cells and erases the contents of the memory. The device can then be reprogrammed with a new combination of charged cells by the PROM programmer. If the EPROM is well protected from ultra-violet light, the memory contents may remain for up to 10 years.

Q2.4, 2.5

2.3   Information transfer

We have seen that information needs to be moved around within the microcomputer (between the memory and the CPU, for example), but have not yet considered how that information might travel. In a microcomputer system data and instructions are transferred backwards and forwards to the CPU along electrical connections known as *buses*. These are usually printed circuit tracks or bundles of wires. As the bus is used for transferring information, the width of the bus, i.e. how many wires, depends on the number of bits in a word, e.g. to move an 8-bit word requires 8 wires on the bus.

An *interface chip* or *input/output chip* is usually used to connect the microprocessor to any external devices or *peripherals*, which are essential if the computer is to communicate with the outside world.

As the name suggests the input/output chip provides an interface or link to external devices. In the next chapter I will explain more fully the problems of connecting the microcomputer to outside peripherals and look at some of the devices that enable us to communicate with the microcomputer.

Q2.6

2.4   Summary

Technological advances have meant that the central processing units (CPUs) of a computer, known as microprocessors, and now complete microcomputers can be built on a single integrated circuit or 'chip' of silicon.

The main components of a microcomputer may be summarised as follows:

● *Microprocessor unit or CPU* which includes with it:
  (a) a control unit
  (b) an arithmetic and logical unit (ALU)
  (c) special-purpose storage registers such as the program counter, accumulator and instruction register.
● *Data memory or RAM* (a read/write memory).
● *Program memory or ROM* (a read only memory). PROMs or EPROMs may be used in development systems to provide more versatility.
● *Input/output* section which deals with interfacing the microcomputer to its external peripherals.
● *Buses* which transfer information around the microcomputer and to and from the peripherals.

Questions

2.1   List the main components of a microcomputer.

2.2 *(a)* What is understood by the *word length* of the microprocessor?

  (b) What is another name for an 8-bit word?

2.3 What is the name of the special register usually used by the ALU?

2.4 What is a RAM and what is it usually used for?

2.5 Name two special types of ROM and explain why they are different from a standard ROM.

2.6 How is information transferred within the microcomputer?

Chapter 3 Peripheral devices

Objectives of this chapter *When you have completed studying this chapter you should be able to:*
1 *Draw a block diagram of a microcomputer which interfaces to the outside world through various peripherals.*
2 *Explain why digital-to-analogue and analogue-to-digital convertors are necessary.*
3 *Identify typical peripheral devices and explain their basic functions.*

Obviously the microcomputer cannot be used unless it has some means of connecting or *interfacing* to the outside world. Information must be fed to the computer by people and machines and the computer must also have some means of transmitting the processed information back to the user. The generalised microcomputer described in the last chapter forms the core of the system shown in Figure 3.1. *Peripheral* devices have been added to the system to enable the necessary communication between the microcomputer and the user. In this chapter I will explain the use of some typical peripheral devices.

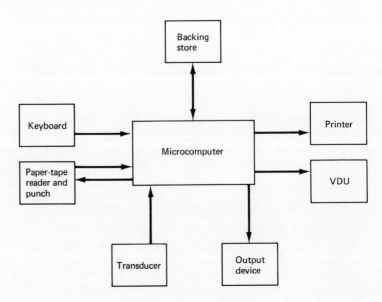

Figure 3.1 A microcomputer with peripherals

Figure 3.2 A full keyboard for a microcomputer *(Courtesy: The Open University)*

3.1 The keyboard

To allow the user to enter information in the form of data or programs, an input device is required. This is normally a keyboard which may consist of anything from a full typewriter keyboard to a simple group of switches (Figures 3.2 and 3.3). The type of keyboard used depends very much on the application. Generally however, a full keyboard is used if there will be a lot of interaction between the user and the microcomputer, and where little interaction is required a simpler set of controls can be used.

Figure 3.3 Microprocessor-based controller for a model railway *(Courtesy: Hornby Hobbies)*

Figure 3.4   Paper tape reader (and printer)

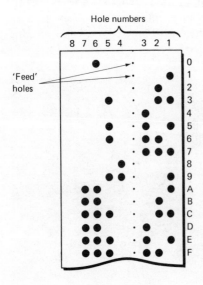

Figure 3.5   Coded paper tape

3.2   Paper-tape reader and punch

An alternative to using a keyboard is to use paper tape pre-punched with information. This can be fed into a paper-tape reader (Figure 3.4) which then interprets the holes in the tape and provides a direct binary information input to the computer.

A paper-tape punch can provide an output from a microcomputer by punching output onto paper tape. These two functions, reading the hole punching, may be incorporated into one machine. Such paper-tape devices are well suited to the binary systems used in micro-computers as they operate on a hole/no hole basis which can be converted electronically to give the two different voltage levels required by the microcomputer. The paper tape commonly used has eight hole positions across its width and another smaller locator hole which helps to feed the tape through the reader. A character or number is represented by a combination of holes across the tape. The coding for these characters varies but one example is given in Figure 3.5. Because this code is different from the 8-bit binary code used by the microprocessor to represent numbers, a special program stored within the microcomputer can be used to automatically interpret the code and perform any necessary conversion. Alternatively a special

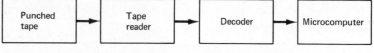

Figure 3.6 Information transfer from tape to microcomputer

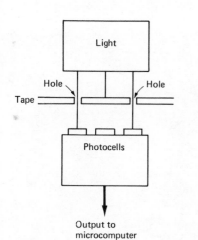

Figure 3.7 Wire brush tape reader

piece of hardware called a decoder may be used as shown in Figure 3.6.

The patterns of holes are read by the paper tape reader in one of two ways. The tape may move over wire brushes (see Figure 3.7) which make contact with a metal plate beneath the tape when a hole is reached. This will produce an output pulse which normally represents binary one. In the other method of reading the punched tape (Figure 3.8), a light source and photocells are used on either side of the tape. Again, a circuit is completed when there is a hole in the tape as the light can hit the photocell beneath and give an output voltage pulse in the form of a binary one.

Q3.2

3.3 Printer

Another device used to aid input and output to the microcomputer is the printer (Figure 3.9). For input information, the microprocessor can arrange to send a copy of all the messages sent to it from the keyboard. This gives a permanent record of the input data or programs. The printer can also be used to record output information from the microcomputer. These machines normally type out the standard alphabet and digits rather than zeros and ones.

There are two main types of printer: the *line-at-a-time* printer which

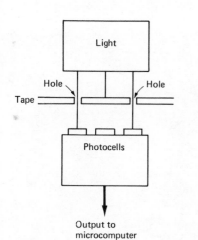

Figure 3.8 Tape reader using photocells

Figure 3.9 Line-at-a-time printer (*Courtesy: Anadex Ltd*)

prints all the characters on a line simultaneously, and the *character-at-a-time* printer which prints in the same way as a typewriter but at much higher speeds. Generally the line-by-line printer is faster.

Because the printer types out information using alphanumeric characters, some form of decoding must be performed on the binary information which comes out of the microcomputer. A 7-bit code known as *ASCII* (American Standard Code for Information Interchange) is usually used to convert from binary code to alphanumeric characters. In this code, binary configurations represent letters, denary digits or punctuation marks.

3.4   Visual display unit

A *visual display unit* (VDU) is used to check the input to the computer as information is keyed in (in much the same way as the printer) and to give an immediate display of the information during processing by the computer. A VDU may be a converted TV receiver, but purpose-built monitors (Figure 3.10) are available, often with keyboards attached.

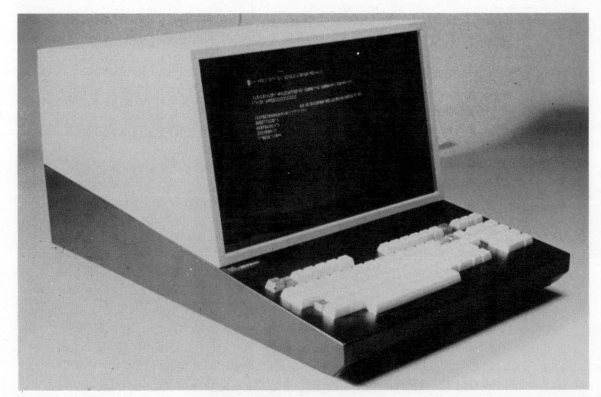

Figure 3.10   Video monitor and keyboard. *(Courtesy: Newbury Laboratories Ltd)*

Figure 3.11   Floppy disk system. *(Courtesy: Sintrom Electronics Ltd)*

The important feature of the VDU is that unlike the printer it only provides a temporary record of input and output to the computer.

3.5   Backing stores

If the microcomputer is handling large amounts of data, it may not have sufficient internal memory in which to store the information. In such cases extra memory in the form of a *backing store* is required. Often, an ordinary audio cassette recorder can be used, with the programs and data recorded on magnetic tape cassettes.

For applications requiring even more storage space or faster information retrieval, a *floppy disk* system may be used (see Figure 3.11). A floppy disk is a magnetic storage device which looks similar to a 45 rpm record. The disks are slotted into a *disk drive* unit which performs the operations necessary to record and recover the information on the disk. Information is stored on the tapes and disks in much the same way as audio signals are recorded on magnetic tape.

Q3.3

3.6   Using transducers

When a microcomputer is being used to control or monitor machinery, it may be used in conjunction with a variety of special

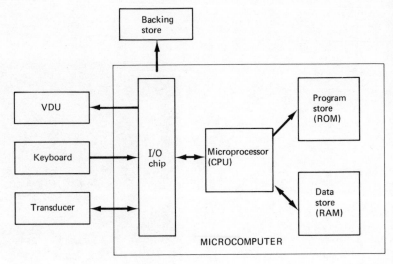

Figure 3.12   Full microcomputer system

peripherals called *transducers*. These devices can convert quantities like temperature, flow rate and motion into electrical voltages. The electrical voltages from any of these devices must be in a form that can be used by the microcomputer. Normally these voltages will vary continuously over a range (like temperature, speed), and are known as *analogue* voltage levels. However, the microcomputer can only work with *digital* information in the form of two distinct voltages, so the analogue signals must be converted to digital form using an *analogue-to-digital converter* (often abbreviated to A to D or A/D converter). In a similar way, if the microcomputer has to drive a motor at a varying speed, or operate a heater over a range of temperature, the signals from the processor must be converted from digital to analogue form using a *digital-to-analogue converter* (D to A, or A/D converter) so that they can drive the output devices. Special interfacing integrated circuits are available for most microprocessors which make the connection of A/D and D/A converters and other peripherals to the microcomputer relatively easy.

Figure 3.12 shows the microprocessor and all the other parts and peripherals we have looked at which enable it to act as a complete microcomputer system.

Q3.1, 3.4

3.7 Summary

1 To communicate with the outside world, the microcomputer must be connected to a variety of peripheral devices.
2 Devices such as visual display units, printers, keyboards and

paper-tape readers and punches are used to communicate between the operator and the computer.

3 Devices such as floppy disks and tape recorders are used to provide extra storage space for programs and data.

4 Transducers and output devices along with their associated analogue-to-digital and digital-to-analogue converters are used to enable the computer to measure and control other devices and processes.

5 Interfacing 'chips' are available which make the connection of peripherals to the computer easier.

Questions

3.1 *(a)* Name two devices which are used to enter information to the microcomputer (input devices)

(b) Name three output devices.

3.2 How is binary information read from paper tape?

3.3 Name two types of backing store.

3.4 *(a)* What is a transducer?

(b) What is a D/A converter and why are they used?

Chapter 4 A microprocessor controlling a system

Objectives of this chapter *When you have completed studying this chapter you should be able to:*

1 *Draw a block diagram of a microprocessor system showing the processor, memory and transducers, and give a written description of the system.*
2 *Explain the method of polling the transducers to obtain information.*
3 *Explain the process by which the processor reacts to information obtained from the transducers.*
4 *State whether, given a description of an input or output device, an analogue-to-digital converter or a digital-to-analogue converter or no converter at all would be required.*

The aim of this chapter is to show you how a microcomputer can be used to control a system, that chosen being a simple cooling system. Before the advent of cheap microprocessors, such systems probably would not have been computer-controlled. In this example the microprocessor has to respond to inputs from several different sources and make different decisions depending upon the value of these inputs.

4.1 System task description

The basic system controls the temperature of two separate devices. These devices generate their own heat and they could be motors or machines, etc., or even a room. A temperature sensor is used to measure the device's temperature and a fan provides any cooling that is required. A diagrammatical representation of the system is shown in Figure 4.1. Major system elements such as the microprocessor are shown, as are the control and data paths between the elements. The paths are shown as lines connecting the system blocks. On these lines are arrow heads representing the direction of flow of the data, i.e. to or from the microprocessor or, as is the case of the line joining the memory to the microprocessor, to *and* from the processor.

This system diagram of Figure 4.1 shows that the microprocessor is controlling two identical processes. This is a fairly common occurrence and indeed in many applications such as this a typical microprocessor could control several more processes.

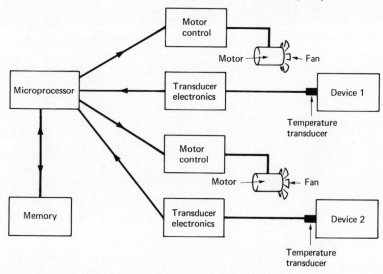

Figure 4.1 A microprocessor-controlled cooling system

The basic control action is as follows. The microprocessor determines the temperature of the device using data from the temperature sensor. It then compares this data with pre-set reference data stored in memory. If the device is above the maximum temperature limit it signals the fan motor to start. The amount by which the device exceeds the required temperature determines the fan speed that the processor selects.

Adjustments to the fan speed will probably be needed only every second or so and therefore the microprocessor which typically performs 1 million basic actions per second will have time to look after the second cooling system as well.

Q4.1, 4.2

4.2 The signals within the system

The data flowing between the processor and the other elements of the system is, of course, binary data as this is the only sort the processor can handle. However, the temperature sensor may well (depending on its type) produce a continuously variable voltage related to the sensed temperature and the motor may be controlled by varying an input voltage. Clearly then, the system diagram of Figure 4.1 should be modified to include the necessary A/D and D/A converters as shown in Figure 4.2.

The processor has to accept binary data from two A/D converters and to send binary data to two D/A converters. Sending data to the D/A converters usually presents no problem to the processor. It can send the data whenever it wants, but some care must be taken to

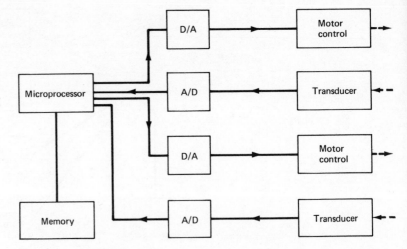

Figure 4.2   A/D and D/A devices are used to interface the processor to the transducers and motors

ensure that the D/A converter has settled to a voltage representing the last data word before the next data word is sent.

However, collecting data from the input transducers and their associated A/D converters can cause some timing problems. The basic reason is that A/D converters take a significant time to perform the conversion from analogue to digital. Moreover, with some types of converter the time taken to perform the conversion depends upon the value of the input voltage. (Usually with this type of converter larger input voltages will require longer conversion times.) Therefore, in this simple system the processor has no way of knowing when the data from the input devices is available.

There are two basic ways in which the processor can handle this problem and these are:

1   By interrogating the transducers; this is termed *polling*.
2   By allowing the transducers to *interrupt* whatever operations the processor is performing.

4.3   Polling the input transducers

In this method the processor systematically and regularly examines the A/D converters associated with the transducers to see if they have recently completed a conversion and have data available.

The diagram of a typical converter in Figure 4.3 shows that there is a connection labelled 'Conversion complete' or 'Data ready'. This connection usually has a binary voltage signal on it which the processor can interpret to determine if data is ready. If data is ready

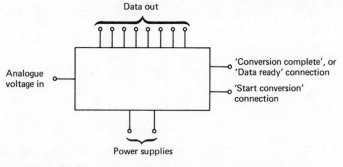

Figure 4.3 An A/D converter showing its principle connections

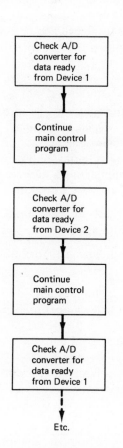

Figure 4.4 Program flow for a temperature control system

Q4.3, 4.4

when the A/D converter is polled, the processor reads the binary pattern of ones and zeros on the 'data out' pins.

Sometimes the A/D converters need to be instructed by the processor to begin a conversion via the 'Start conversion' connection. A system that requires such instruction will be described later in this book, but for the moment let us assume that the converters do not require a specific command from the processor to start.

The flow of the program for the temperature control system outlined above and which uses polling is shown diagrammatically in Figure 4.4 The two temperature transducers are regularly examined or polled to see if they contain new data. One obvious feature of this polling system is that the processor must regularly stop what it is doing to examine the converters without any certainty that the converter has data available. This is obviously wasteful of the processor's time. If the processor is not very busy this may not matter, but if it is, this potential waste of time may cause problems. Furthermore, if the processor is busy the frequency that it can check on the converter may not be fast enough.

The second method of obtaining data is to allow the input device to interrupt the processor when it has data for the processor. This is obviously more efficient from the point of view of not wasting the processor's time, but it does raise other problems. Some of these will be discussed in Chapter 5.

4.4 Summary

1 A microcomputer system can be used to control another system involving (in the example described) temperature sensors and fans. However, a microcomputer system can, in general, control systems with a variety of transducers.
2 Analogue-to-digital and digital-to-analogue converters may well be needed as an interface between the processor and various input and output devices.

3   One method of microprocessor control involves the processor comparing received data with certain reference data stored in the memory. The results of this comparison determine what the processor does next.

4   The processor can handle the inputs from several transducers by either polling them regularly or allowing them to interrupt it.

Questions

4.1   Sketch a block diagram similar to Figure 4.2 for a microprocessor-controlled greenhouse-climate control system. The inputs to the system are temperature, soil moisture and sunlight intensity. The outputs are an on/off control to the water sprinkler system and a variable control voltage to air conditioning fans. Indicate which of the input/output devices requires A/D or D/A converters.

4.2   Describe a strategy for controlling the temperature and moisture in a system such as that described in Question 4.1.

4.3   State two problems associated with the polling method of obtaining input data.

4.4   State the type of convertor required, if any, for the following devices:
(a)   a temperature transducer with an output voltage proportional to temperature;
(b)   a heating element controlled by an applied voltage;
(c)   an on/off switch;
(d)   a load-cell, i.e. a device whose output is a voltage proportional to the weight of material placed upon it.

Chapter 5 The use of interrupts in a microcomputer controller

Objectives of this chapter *When you have completed studying this chapter you should be able to:*
1 *Describe the operations to be performed by the processor when it is interrupted.*
2 *Give a description of an input device, decide whether it is generally more appropriate to use polling or interrupts.*

The aim of this chapter is to show you how information can be obtained from external devices by allowing them to interrupt the normal operation of the program. Programs that are written to allow this process are called interrupt-driven programs and many types of microprocessors have design features which help the writing of such software.

5.1 A more complex temperature control system

To illustrate the action of an input device which interrupts the micro-computer let us look at the system shown in Figure 5.1. This is slightly

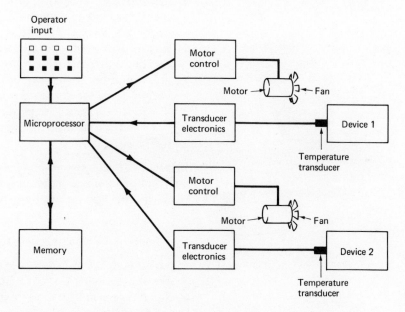

Figure 5.1 Temperature control system with a keyboard peripheral

more complex than that considered earlier. Notice that the system diagram has been expanded to include a keyboard which is used to input data into the processor. Using this keyboard an operator can change the reference data in the memory and enable the temperatures at which the devices are maintained to be changed. Obviously, if there is to be a change in temperature it is important that the processor is aware of the change as quickly as possible. Therefore the input keyboard would probably be allowed to interrupt the processor at any time using an interrupt signal.

Different processors require different forms of interrupt signal, but the principle is the same for many microprocessors. The microprocessor will have a connection which is used to sense an interrupt. An interrupt will be sensed as a change from 1 to 0 or 0 to 1 on this connection, depending on the type of processor.

5.2   On receipt of an interrupt

Suppose in our system the operator decides to change some of the data in memory. Then the action of pressing one of the keys will send an interrupt signal to the processor. The following actions then take place:

1   The processor stops what it is doing at that moment.
2   The data in the processor's internal storage locations (registers) which is relevant to the operation that has been interrupted must be stored in the main memory.
3   The processor must also store the information which will enable the program to continue at the point it was interrupted once the operator's changes have been made.
4   If more than one device is allowed to interrupt, the processor must find out which device has caused the interrupt. (There is considerable variation in the way different processors do this.) In the example only the keyboard can interrupt so there is no problem.
5   The processor must then perform the piece of program which has been incorporated in the software to handle this particular interrupting device.

Figure 5.2 illustrates how the main program must jump to the interrupt-handling program segment as soon as an interrupt is **Q5.1**   received. This may occur at any time in the main program.

5.3   Interrupt-handling segment for the temperature controller

In our example the processor must stop what it is doing on receipt of an interrupt from the keyboard, store any current data and then go to a program segment which interprets the signals coming from the keyboard. If, for example, the operator wants to change the controlled

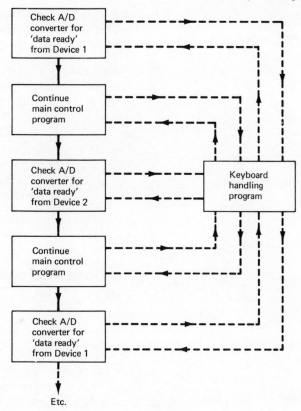

Figure 5.2 Program flow after an interrupt

temperature for device 1, the processor must recognise this and put new data in the relevant part of memory which is used when controlling the temperature of device 1. When this modification has been made, the processor returns to its previous task.

5.4 Systems with more than one interface device allowed to interrupt

This is obviously the more general case and does pose the problem outlined above that the processor must determine which device has produced the interrupt signal. There are basically two ways in which the processor does this.

One way (used by the Motorola 6800 type of microprocessor) is that as soon as an interrupt is received, all of the possible sources of the interrupt are polled to see which one has caused it.

The other way (used by the 8080 processor) is to require the interrupting device to send a code, unique to itself, to the processor after it has been interrupted. This code is interpreted by the processor and the correct interrupt-servicing routine implemented.

As soon as there is more than one source for an interrupt further potential complications can occur. What happens, for instance, if two interrupts occur together? Or if another interrupt occurs before the processor has finished handling the first? The answer is that the processor must assign priorities to the interrupts and deal with the most important first. Complications such as these mean that the program controlling the response to interrupts gets complex. Also, since the interrupts can occur at any time in the main program and in any order, it is impossible to test all the variations of interrupts and main program position that can occur.

Despite all the problems raised by using interrupts they tend to be essential for devices which demand quick attention.

5.5 Polling versus interrupts

Polling input transducers regularly is simple, but it may not be possible to poll fast transducers sufficiently quickly. Moreover, polling can mean the processor wasting time testing devices that have no data available.

The use of interrupts ensures a faster response to input devices but requires more complex programs, especially if there is more than one source of interrupt.

Q5.2

5.6 Summary

1   Devices that require a fast response from the processor will tend to use interrupts.
2   When a processor receives an interrupt it must save all relevant data needed to return to the main program after it has handled the interrupt.
3   The use of interrupts often tends to complicate the program.

Questions

5.1   List the operations to be performed by a microprocessor when it receives an interrupt.

5.2   State for the following input devices whether the microprocessor is more likely to use polling or allow interrupts:
  (a) a cassette tape providing data at 300 bits per second;
  (b) a load cell producing data via an A/D converter every 5 seconds;
  (c) an emergency shut-down switch.

Chapter 6 Maintenance of microprocessor-based systems

Objectives of this chapter *When you have completed studying this chapter you should be able to:*

1 *Distinguish between hardware and software faults.*
2 *Describe in general terms the sorts of maintenance aids available for microprocessor systems.*

The aim of this chapter is to show you that the detection of faults in microprocessor-based systems requires special test equipment and special test computer programs.

6.1 Hardware or software fault?

Often the question whether a fault is due to hardware or software is the first problem to confront the maintenance engineer as some faults are not easily related to one or the other.

Suppose that in our example the fault was that the operator could not get the microprocessor to respond to the keyboard. This could be a hardware fault in that the keyboard was not sending the correct interrupt signal or the processor was not interpreting the correct signal as an interrupt.

Alternatively, the software could be incorrect and not servicing the interrupt correctly. A final, more subtle, fault could be that a hardware fault in part of the memory storing the program produces a faulty program – a hardware fault causing what looks to be a software fault!

The point is that by just looking at the symptom it is very difficult to tell if the hardware or software is at fault. Instead special maintenance tools designed for microprocessors must be used.

You may well be wondering why a maintenance person would have to modify faulty software – surely it is the job of the programmer to get it right before the product is sent to the customer?

In practice, the programmer should make every effort to ensure the program is correct, but with large programs requiring, say, more than 100 hours to write, program faults are almost certain. Errors will continue to be found occasionally for some time during commission-

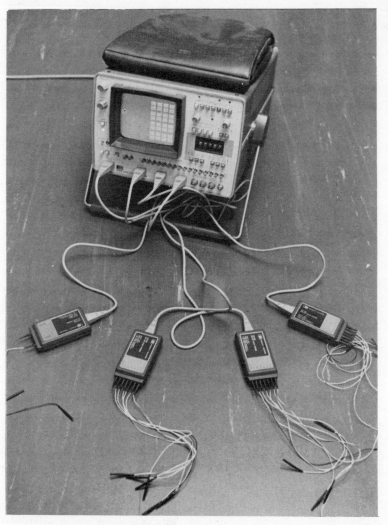

Figure 6.1 A logic analyser

ing of the equipment. As I explained earlier, one of the reasons for this is that programs with interrupts are difficult to test fully.

6.2 Maintenance aids

The first point to stress in this section is that conventional maintenance aids such as oscilloscopes and multimeters are on their own of limited use in the detection of faults in a microprocessor system. This is because the oscilloscopes can only be used to look at three or four signals at a time but with a microprocessor perhaps 40 signals may be important at any one time. Instead, oscilloscopes have a useful function only when used in conjunction with special-purpose microprocessor maintenance aids.

Maintenance aids fall into two basic classes:

1 Self-diagnostic programs
2 Logic analysers

Self-diagnostic programs are special programs which the maintenance person can run on the actual equipment on test provided the processor itself is not completely faulty. A typical program for our temperature control example may well test the following:

1 That the memory is behaving correctly.
2 The processor is able to address the memory correctly.
3 That the data and interrupts from the interface devices are being recognised correctly.

This test is, of course, not complete and the degree of self-testing ability depends on the complexity of the test program. Often test programs of sufficient complexity can pin-point the fault exactly and the necessary hardware replaced or software rewritten.

Special hardware aids called logic analysers are also available to detect faults in microprocessor systems. Figure 6.1 shows one of these aids which is used to look at the binary signals in parts of the microprocessor system. Often they enable not only the signals present in the system at the moment the fault appears to be displayed but also those signals that led up to the fault. This is a most useful feature because often the actual fault occurs sometime before the symptom.

However, because these logic analysers cost several thousand pounds their use is often restricted to the design and development phase of the product and maintenance is usually performed using special-purpose diagnostic programs in conjunction with simple test equipment such as oscilloscopes.

Q6.1

6.3 Summary

1 Microprocessor systems are prone to both hardware and software faults which at first sight may be difficult to distinguish.
2 Self-testing diagnostic programs are often used to detect the cause of a fault.
3 Hardware testing aids such as logic analysers are often only used in the design and development phase of a product.

Question

6.1 Explain the difference between hardware and software faults.

Chapter 7 **Microprocessor programming**

Objectives of this chapter *When you have completed studying this chapter you should be able to:*

1 *Recognise the differences between machine code, assembler and high-level language programs.*
2 *List the features of assembler programming.*
3 *Express binary numbers in both octal and hexadecimal forms.*

The aim of this chapter is to explain the ways in which a microcomputer system can be programmed and the relative merits of machine code, assembler and high-level languages.

7.1 Microcomputer programming

Up until now I have described the hardware of a microcomputer system and the way in which the program controls its operation. In this chapter I intend to introduce you to the way in which a microprocessor program is produced.

Remember that the program for a microprocessor will usually be stored in a read only memory or ROM. The form that the program takes within the ROM depends on the type of the ROM: it may be represented as voltages or blown fuses. However, from the programmer's point of view the way in which it is stored is largely unimportant.

What is important is how the ones and zeros comprising the program are organised within the memory. For an 8-bit microprocessor the memory is arranged so that each memory location contains a pattern of eight ones and zeros called an 8-bit word. The computer operates under the control of the microprocessor by reading these memory locations in the appropriate sequence and performing the implied operations.

The programmer's job is to produce the correct patterns of ones and zeros in the correct sequence so as to carry out the required task. At a basic level this consists of the programmer consulting manufacturers' data to find the binary pattern required in each memory location. Table 7.1 shows what a completed segment of the program looks like. This program can then be written into the memory either by the manufacturer of the memory chip or using a PROM programmer as mentioned earlier.

This type of programming in which the programmer has to remember, or find from a data book, the pattern of bits required for each operation is called *machine code programming*.

The basic operations available to the programmer are different from one microprocessor to another and even the same operations on different microprocessors require different binary patterns. Consequently machine code programming is a skilled and tedious operation. There are plenty of opportunities for error, and error-free programs of a hundred memory locations or more are extremely difficult to produce.

What is required is a comparatively easily remembered form of shorthand for the patterns corresponding to the instructions available for a particular microprocessor. This would still leave the data as a binary pattern so we need a shorthand for that as well.

7.2 Assembler programming

Assembler programming enables a programmer to use a shorthand representation for the instructions and, as I shall describe later, the data. First though, consider the following example.

CMA is the assembler shorthand for an instruction for the 8080 microprocessor. This instruction causes the microprocessor to CoMplement, i.e. change, all the ones to zeros and all the zeros to ones in a temporary storage location within the processor called the Accumulator. This means that if the contents of the accumulator before the instruction is carried out is the word 00001111, then

Table 7.1

Contents	Address number
1 1 0 0 1 1 1 0	0
1 1 1 1 1 1 1 1	1
0 0 0 0 0 1 0 0	2
1 1 1 1 1 1 1 1	3
1 0 0 0 0 0 0 0	4
0 0 1 0 0 0 0 0	5
1 1 0 0 1 1 1 0	6
0 0 0 0 0 0 0 0	7
0 0 1 0 1 0 0 1	8

afterwards it becomes 11110000. Notice that I have capitalised the three letters in the instruction 'CoMplement the Accumulator' which make up the instruction CMA. Because the shorthand, CMA, is related to the instruction in this way it serves as an aid to the memory and for this reason it is called a *mnemonic*. All of the possible instructions for the 8080 have similar mnemonics and are therefore easier to remember than the binary patterns.

For example, CMA and 00101111 both represent the instruction 'complement the accumulator' of an 8080, but the binary code is far more difficult to remember or even to write down.

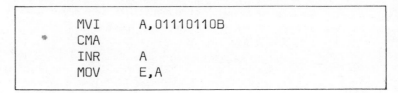

```
        MVI     A,01110110B
  *     CMA
        INR     A
        MOV     E,A
```

Figure 7.1   A segment of assembler program

A typical piece of an assembler program with a few of these mnemonics is shown in Figure 7.1. Do not worry at this stage that you do not understand all of the mnemonics in this example. I am only concerned that you begin to recognise the difference between a machine code and an assembler program. However, a brief description of the program in Figure 7.1 will help you see the relationship between the mnemonics and the instructions they represent.

Line 1   MoVe Immediate, into the Accumulator the Binary data 01110110.
Line 2   CoMplement the Accumulator.
Line 3   INcrement the data in the Register called the Accumulator by one.
Line 4   MOVe into the E register the data in the Accumulator.

Again I have capitalised the letters that occur in the mnemonic.

In summary then, assembler programming allows the programmer to write a program using mnemonics, which, because they are an abbreviated version of the operation performed by the instruction, are easier to remember and less likely to be used in error than the binary patterns used in machine code programming.

The assembler program still requires converting into a pattern of ones and zeros to be stored in a ROM. This conversion can be done by hand by the programmer using manufacturers' data which lists the binary code for each mnemonic. Although this is a simple, if repetitive, task it is prone to error and instead a special computer program is usually used to do this conversion. The program used is called an *assembler program*.

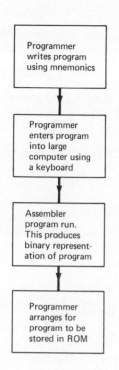

Figure 7.2 shows the sequence of steps that are performed to program a microprocessor using one of these assembler programs.

The instructions available for the programmer are different on different microprocessors so the programmer has to use an assembler program specially written for the microprocessor he is using. Nowadays there are many assembler programs available and they can be run on many different types of computer. In some cases it is possible to run an assembler program on the microcomputer system the final program is being developed for.

There are, however, many advantages to using large computers to run the assembler programs. One of these advantages is that large machines enable the programmer to input and, if necessary, correct his program comparatively easily.

Before I explain how data as well as instructions can be written in a shorthand form in assembler programming I want to stress one final advantage that is gained by getting a computer to convert the mnemonics. When a computer performs the conversion using an assembler program it continually checks to see if the mnemonics have been used correctly within the program. If there are any errors it informs the programmer and correction is then comparatively easy.

Figure 7.2 The production of program using an assembler

7.3 Data representation

Assembler programming as I have described it up until now enables 'shorthand notation' to be used for the instructions but it still requires the data to be represented as binary numbers. However, there are two 'shorthand' ways of representing these binary numbers for handling by assembler programs. These are called *octal* and *hexadecimal* representation.

Octal

In octal, or base 8, representation the binary digits are grouped in threes and the value of each group written down. For example, in Figure 7.3 the binary number is 10111001 and the grouping is started from the right (the least most significant digit end).

The first group on the right is 001 and its value

$$(0 \times 2^2) + (0 \times 2^1) + (1 \times 2^0) = 1$$

The next grouping is 111 and its value is

$$(1 \times 2^2) + (1 \times 2^1) + (1 \times 2^0) = 7$$

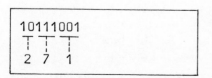

Figure 7.3 Octal representation

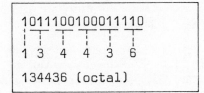

Figure 7.4 Octal representation

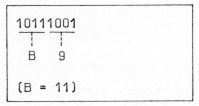

Figure 7.5 Hexadecimal representation

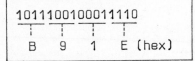

Figure 7.6 Hexadecimal representation

The final group, 10, has only two digits, because the original word was 8 bits long, and its value is

$$(1 \times 2^1) + (0 \times 2^0) = 2$$

The resulting octal representation of this word is 271_8. I have written the subscript 8 after the number as it is important to make clear the actual representation being used for a binary number.

Figure 7.4 gives a further example of octal representation this time for a 16-bit word.

Hexadecimal

Hexadecimal, or base 16, is very similar to octal except that (as Figure 7.5 shows) the digits are grouped together four at a time. The least significant group is 1001 and this has the value

$$(1 \times 2^3) + (0 \times 2^2) + (0 \times 2^1) + (1 \times 2^0) = 9$$

The next grouping is 1011 and this has the value

$$(1 \times 2^3) + (0 \times 2^2) + (1 \times 2^1) + (1 \times 2^0) = 11$$

However, this number is not used in hexadecimal because it could be confusing; it could also be interpreted as representing two groups each with the value 1. Instead the letters A,B,C,D,E and F are used to represent 10,11,12,13,14 and 15, respectively. Thus 11 is written as B. The hexadecimal representation of 10111001 is therefore B9 (hex). [Note that 'hexadecimal' is usually abbreviated to (hex).]

Figure 7.6 shows a further example of hexadecimal representation, this time for a 16-bit number.

Assembler programs can handle hexadecimal, octal and binary representations of data, but the programmer must specify which he is using. This usually involves using a special character either immediately before or after the data. For example one type of 8080 assembler program recognises data followed by a B as binary, data followed by an H as hexadecimal and data followed by O as octal. (If

```
MVI     A,166O              MVI     A,76H
CMA                         CMA
INR     A                   INR     A
MOV     E,A                 MOV     E,A

(a) octal                   (b) hex
```

Figure 7.7 Examples of *(a)* octal and *(b)* hexadecimal representation in a program written in assembler

the hexadecimal number starts with a letter, the 8080 assembler requires that a zero be placed in front of it. For example,

```
MVI  A,0A7H;
```

Figure 7.7 shows the same assembler program segment shown earlier but with hexadecimal and octal representations of the data.

Q7.4

7.4 High-level language programming

In addition to machine code and assembler programming there is one other commonly used method of writing programs for micro-processors. This method is called high-level language programming.

```
K:=0
for I:=1 to 10 do K:=K+I;
```

Figure 7.8 A high-level language program

Figure 7.8 shows two lines from a high-level program written in PASCAL.

On first sight this type of language is still difficult to interpret but if I explain what these lines mean you should be able to realise that this type of programming language is more compact and closer to speech than either machine code or assembler code.

The first line of the program makes the variable $K = 0$ and the second line adds together all of the numbers between 1 and 10. The second line is, in fact, repetitive in that it instructs the computer to add the value of I to K, call the result the new value of K and then increment the value of I by 1. This is repeated ten times. The resulting value of K is $1 + 2 + 3 + 4 + 5 + 6 + 7 + 8 + 9 + 10$ which equals 55.

Of course, this type of high-level program still has to be converted into ones and zeros and this is done in a similar way to assembler programs by using another computer program to do the conversion.

You may be asking why, if this type of programming is so powerful, is assembler programming used at all? The answer is that programs written in high-level languages usually require more memory to store them once they have been converted to ones and zeros and also take longer to run than programs written using an assembler. Often this is not important and more and more programs for microcomputers are being written in a high-level language because they are easier to write, check and maintain.

Q7.1, 7.2

Summary

1   There are three main ways of programming a microcomputer. These are by using:
    (a)   machine code;
    (b)   an assembler;
    (c)   a high-level language.
2   In machine code programming the programmer enters ones and zeros representing the program into memory, often using a PROM programmer. To find the correct pattern of ones and zeros, the programmer must consult manufacturers' data.
3   Assembler programming enables the programmer to use a shorthand notation for the instructions, mnemonics, and a shorthand for the data, either octal or hex. An assembler program converts these to the required ones and zeros and checks for errors.
4   High-level language is the easiest to write because it is most like speech. It too requires conversion to ones and zeros and the resulting programs tend to be longer and slower than those written in assembler or machine code.

Questions

7.1   Identify the types of program shown in Figure A.

```
(a)    MOV      C,A
       MVI      B,00H
       CMA

(b)    If (X<0) or Y(>0) then
          begin
            for I:=1 to max
            X:=X+1
             END;

(c)    Contents    Address
       11110011    1
       11111101    2
       10101010    3
```

Figure A

7.2   What are the advantages of assembler programming compared with machine code programming?

7.3   Convert the following binary numbers:

    10110000
    11111111
    00000000
    10101010

into

(a)   octal;
(b)   hexadecimal.

7.4   Convert the following numbers in 8-bit binary words:
(a)   15
(b)   15 (hex)
(c)   157 (octal).

Chapter 8 A register model of a microprocessor

Objectives of this chapter *When you have completed studying this chapter you should be able to:*

1 *Sketch a register model for a microprocessor and explain the purpose of the various registers.*
2 *Describe the general types of microprocessor instructions.*
3 *Explain the purpose of various registers within the processor.*

The aim of this chapter is to describe in more detail the internal organisation and workings of a microprocessor. I will concentrate on the 8080 microprocessor as an example, but much of the chapter is relevant to other types of processor.

8.1 The model

As I have explained before, the internal structure of a microprocessor differs with different makes of microprocessor. I intend to describe a model which is applicable to the 8080 and 8085 microprocessors, but my description will introduce ideas that relate to other types of microprocessors. The model is shown in Figure 8.1. One of the most noticeable things about this figure is the rectangular boxes labelled B,C,H,L, etc. These represent 8-bit memory locations within the CPU itself. These memory locations are called registers and they are called the H register, the D register, etc., according to the labels on the figure. The only exceptions to this are the two registers at the top of the diagram. These are called the accumulator and flag registers and they have a rather special function which I will be explaining shortly.

The registers in the microprocessor are of the RAM type, i.e. their contents can be changed during the operation of the processor. Indeed, it is through the manipulation of data within these registers that the microprocessor can function.

Notice that I have shown the wires connecting the CPU to the associated memory and input/output devices as three buses. The address bus is the group of wires that is used to address, for retrieval or storage purposes, a particular memory location. Almost all 8-bit microprocessors use 16 binary digits to address the memory. This

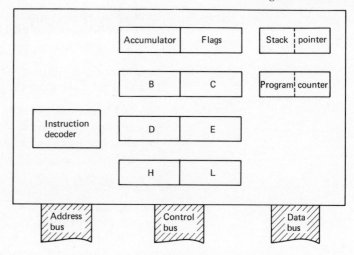

Q8.1   *Figure 8.1*   A register model for the 8080 microprocessor

usually means that the address bus consists of 16 wires. However, some microprocessors use just 8 wires and the 16-bit address is sent as two 8-bit words, one after the other.

The control bus consists of wires that the CPU uses, amongst other things, to inform the memory whether a read or a write is taking place. Another function of the control bus may be to control input and output devices.

The data bus is used to pass binary words to and from the CPU and memory and the CPU and input/output devices. In an 8-bit microprocessor the data bus transmits 8 bits at a time and so consists of 8 wires.

There is one further important part of the CPU shown on Figure 8.1. This is the *instruction decoder* and to explain its purpose I need to remind you of the cycle executed when the CPU is operating under control of a program. Remember that the program is stored in memory (usually ROM) so the first operation of the CPU is to address the memory location that contains the required program instruction. This instruction, which is of course a pattern of ones and zeros, is placed on the data bus so that the CPU can read this instruction. The instruction decoder and control circuitry interprets this pattern and performs the necessary actions. This may involve altering the contents of the registers in the CPU or fetching a data word from a RAM location.

How would this last task be achieved?

The instruction would have associated with it the address of the RAM location and this address would be placed on the address bus along with a signal on the control bus indicating a read operation.

In summary, the instruction decode and control circuit interprets the instructions and controls the internal operation of the CPU. It is, if you like, the portion of the CPU that controls 'how it ticks'.

Before I finish describing this model and examine how the microprocessor can be programmed, it is necessary to describe the registers and their purpose in a little more detail.

General-purpose registers

Six registers, namely the B,C,D,E,H and L registers, are termed general-purpose registers. They are used for intermediate calculations of the processor or to store addresses for data. The H and L registers, taken together, are most often used for this last purpose for a reason which will become apparent later in this chapter.

The program counter register

This consists of two 8-bit registers so that it has the capacity to store 16 bits. It is used specifically to enable the processor to keep track of the memory location in which the next instruction to be fetched and executed is stored.

Remember that the processor operates by progressing logically through a sequence of instructions. It is therefore important for the processor to keep track of the place it has reached in the sequence. The operation of the processor proceeds by decoding the instruction performing the implied operations and then updating the address stored in the program counter so that the next instruction can be fetched. Often this will involve incrementing the contents of the program counter by one or two, but if a subroutine is called (as described in Chapter 9) the CPU will set the program counter to the address of the start of the subroutine. Do not worry if you cannot see exactly how the CPU can keep track in this way as it is largely outside the scope of this book. There is one important point, however, and this is that the CPU does this by itself. The programmer does not need to instruct the CPU to keep track of the next instruction to be executed. It is all automatic; if the programmer writes the code correctly, the correct operation of the program counter will be obtained.

The stack pointer register

This also consists of two 8-bit registers and is therefore capable of storing 16 bits. Its purpose is to enable the CPU to allow the programmer to use subroutines in his program. I will explain how in Chapter 9.

The accumulator and flag registers

The accumulator is an 8-bit register and it has associated with it a register termed the flag register. The purpose of the accumulator is to perform many of the arithmetical and logical operations such as addition and subtraction.

An example of such an arithmetical operation is the addition of two 8-bit binary numbers, the result being stored in the accumulator itself. If the numbers were such that the result was larger than 255, nine bits would be required to represent it but only eight are available in the accumulator. This could lead to errors. Usually what happens therefore is that the eight least significant bits are stored in the accumulator and one of the bits in the flag register is changed to indicate that in reality a 9-bit result has been obtained.

I will be introducing uses of the flag register in Chapter 9, although I will not be explaining all of the uses of the flag register – only those that are useful for the purpose of this book.

For a complete treatment of the use of flags and for a more detailed model of the CPU you may like to consult L.A. Leventhal, *Introduction to microprocessors: software, hardware programming*, Prentice Hall (1978).

8.2 Models for other microprocessors

The model I have been describing is for the 8080 and 8085 microprocessors, but models have been produced for other microprocessors. Figure 8.2 shows models for the Z80 and 6800 microprocessors. They differ in detail from the 8080 model, but notice that they all have a register or registers that can act as an accumulator, a stack pointer and a program counter. Notice too that the memory addresses require 16 bits and the data is in 8-bit groups.

8.3 Microprocessor instructions

As I have mentioned before, different microprocessors have different instructions, but there are general requirements for all microprocessors and these are that they must have the following classes of instruction.

Data movement instructions

These are instructions that move 8-bit data words between the processor and memory locations and between registers in the CPU.

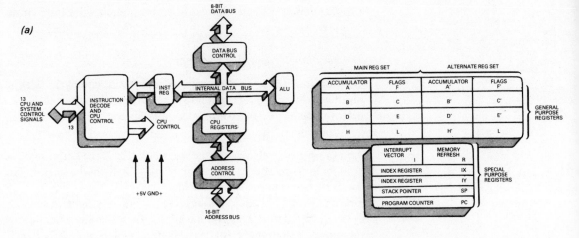

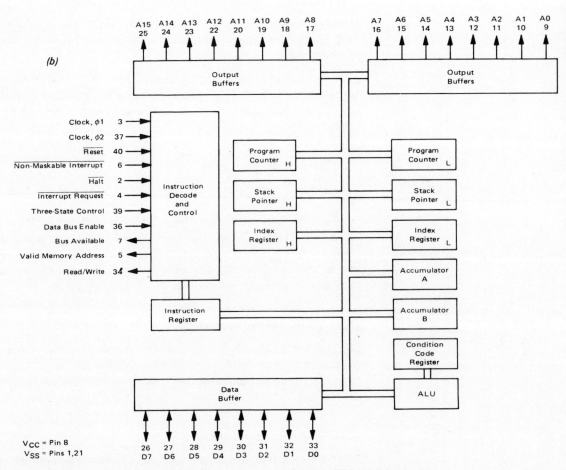

Figure 8.2   Register models for (a) the Z80 microprocessor and (b) the 6800 microprocessor

Input and output instructions

These are instructions that allow the input or output of data to and from the processor and external devices. For example, an input instruction would be required to obtain data from an A/D converter and an output instruction would be required to send data to a display device such as a digital display of the type used on watches.

Arithmetical instructions

These are instructions that perform arithmetical instructions such as the addition and subtraction of binary numbers, or complementing a binary word (remember the CMA instruction in the last chapter)..

Logical instructions

These are instructions that perform logical operations such as AND and OR. Figure 8.3 gives an example of both of these processes.

Test instructions

These are instructions that test the contents of the flag register – remember the test to see if the result of an addition is greater than 8 bits. Another common test is to find out if the contents of the accumulator are zero.

Ultimately it is instructions of this type that allow the use of sub-routines and program loops. This last programming technique will be explained by an example later in Chapter 9.

Q8.2–8.4

```
(a)  ANDING

     Word 1   10011101
     Word 2   00011010

     Result   00011000

(b)  ORING

     Word 1   10011101
     Word 2   00011010

     Result   10011111
```

Figure 8.3 Examples of (a) ANDing and (b) ORing two eight-bit words

8.4 Summary

1 Inside the microprocessor's CPU there are several special- and general-purpose storage locations called registers. The operation of the processor involves manipulation of data between these registers and between memory and these registers.

2 Data and instruction transfers between the CPU and memory or interface components is achieved using the address, data and control buses.

3 In an 8-bit microprocessor the data bus is 8 bits wide and the address bus is usually 16 bits wide.

4 The B,C,D,E,H and L registers are general purpose but usually H and L together are used to store memory addresses.

5 The program counter register is used to control the execution of the program and ensures that the next instruction to be executed is fetched from the correct memory location.

6 The stack pointer register is used to control the temporary storage of the registers during a subroutine call.

7 The accumulator and flag registers are used in general-purpose arithmetical operations.

8 The five main types of microprocessor instruction are:
(a) Data movement instruction.
(b) Input and output instructions.
(c) Arithmetical instructions.
(d) Logical instructions.
(e) Test and jump instructions.

Questions

8.1 Without looking back at the relevant diagram, sketch a register model of the 8080 microprocessor.

8.2 List the five general types of microprocessor instruction.

8.3 What is the purpose of the stack pointer register?

8.4 What is the purpose of the program counter register?

Chapter 9 Assembler programming

Objectives of this chapter *When you have completed studying this chapter you should be able to:*

1 *Give examples of assembler instructions.*
2 *Produce flow diagrams and assembler instructions for short segments of program.*
3 *Describe some of the uses of labels.*

The aim of this chapter is to introduce you to some of the techniques of assembler programming. It is not the intention of this chapter or indeed this book to give a comprehensive description of programming but the examples given in this chapter should help you appreciate what microprocessor assembler programming involves. Most of the programming examples use the 8080 microprocessor, but mention of other processors will be made. However, by far the most important thing that you should get from this chapter is an understanding of the techniques of programming rather than a detailed knowledge of any one microprocessor.

9.1 The form of assembler statements

The assembler instructions that follow are for 8080/8085 processors, but many other processors have instructions which are similar but may have different names. By concentrating on just one type of processor I hope to avoid confusion caused by swapping between processor types. Furthermore, in my experience, once you have understood a group of the instructions and mnemonics for the processor it becomes easier to learn the instructions for other types.

I will introduce each of the instructions in terms of its mnemonic used for assembler programming. This will enable me to give you more examples of assembler-level programming so that by the end of the chapter you should be able to write short assembler-level programs. I will not be explaining all of the instructions for the processor, although they are contained in the Appendix. The ones that I introduce will be those needed for the case study in the next chapter.

9.2 Assembler programming examples

The assembler instruction for complementing the accumulator that I

Label	Opcode	Operand	Comment
LOOP2:	MVI	A,0FFH	;load accumulator with

Figure 9.1 The four fields of a line of a program written in assembler

used in Chapter 7 consisted of just the mnemonic CMA. However, in general, a line of an assembler program would have four distinct parts – see Figure 9.1. These four parts are called *fields* and they are separated by special characters called *delimiters*. There are about a dozen delimiters allowed by most 8080 assembler programs but luckily we need only to consider four main ones and these are:

Space   :   ;   ,

Why must delimiters be used? If you remember back to the explanation of an assembler program you should remember that the assembler is a computer program that converts assembler program statements into binary code. The computer 'reads' the program line by line and its needs to keep track of where one field ends and another begins. So it 'looks' for these special delimiter symbols to indicate the end of one field and the start of the next.

The right-hand-most field of the program line is the *comment field* and it is this field that the programmer can use to explain how the program works and the intended function of any program line. It is extremely important that an assembler program has plenty of informative comments. They help other programmers understand the function of the program and help the original programmer remember the function of the program when examining the program sometime after it has been written.

The comment field is started by the delimiter ; .

The *opcode field* is the field in which the programmer writes the assembler mnemonic for the microprocessor instruction to be performed.

Figure 9.2 shows an example of a line of program which uses the opcode and comment fields. From this example you can see that the label and operand field can be empty. Indeed only the opcode field must contain a mnemonic in each statement.

Label	Opcode	Operand	Comment
	CMA		;complement the accumulator

Figure 9.2 A line of program using only *opcode* and *comment* fields

The *label field* is always optional but as I will show later it has some very important uses. Basically it is used to name a line in the program, names like START, IDLE, and ATOD are used. Numbers alone are not normally used because they are less informative than properly chosen labels.

The label if present can consist of up to six characters and the field is delimited with a :, i.e. ended by a colon.

The *operand field* is required for those instructions which require to specify the data or the location of the data, which will be operated upon. An example is in the transfer of data between CPU and memory or between registers in the CPU.

A program line with all the fields full is shown below

Label	Opcode	Operand	Comment
START:	MOV	A,C	;an example using all
			;four fields

Another example of a program line containing both opcode and operands was shown in Figure 7.1.

This first instruction was

Label	Opcode	Operand	Comment
	MVI	A,01110110B	

This instruction moves the binary number 01110110 into the accumulator. Notice that as in the previous example the two operands are separated by a comma and the destination register is written first. Also notice that the opcode and the operands are separated by several spaces (one is the minimum number).

9.3 Assembler instructions in more detail

The MVI instruction

The first assembler instructions I am going to describe are those that facilitate the storage of specific binary numbers directly into one of the registers in the CPU. For the 8080 assembler this instruction has the mnemonic MVI, and the format of a program line containing this instruction is:

Label	Opcode	Operand	Comment
	MVI	reg,data	

The mnemonic stands for MoVe Immediate. The first operand must be one of the registers in the CPU to which the data is to be moved. The allowed destination registers are A,B,C,D,E,H and L. The second operand is the actual data to be moved into the register. This consists of a binary number which may be written in hex, octal or binary as described in Chapter 7.

Some examples are shown below

```
MVI     A,10000001B     ;binary number to
                        ;accumulator
MVI     B,81H           ;hex number to register B
MVI     D,2010          ;octal number to register D
```

The MVI instruction is therefore a convenient way of loading data into the registers in the CPU. In a slightly modified form it can be used to load data into memory locations. The form of the instruction is then:

```
Opcode  Operand
MVI     M,data
```

The data can be in the same form as before. But there is no M register, so what does this mean? The 'M' is a shorthand which the assembler program interprets as 'send the data to the memory location whose address is the 16 bits stored in the H, L registers.' For example:

```
MVI     M,81H           ;move 81H to memory
```

If the contents of the H,L registers were 0100 (hex) the number 81 (hex) would be stored in the memory location 0100 (hex).

This begs the question. How is the address stored in the H,L registers? It can be done with two MVI instructions:

```
MVI     H,01H           ;load most significant
                        ;eight bits
MVI     L,00H           ;load least significant
                        ;eight bits
```

There are instructions that allow 16 bits to be loaded at a time but, in the interests of clarity, I do not intend to describe them.

The MOV instruction

This instruction copies one 8-bit word, or *byte*, of data from one register to another register within the CPU or, in a slightly modified form, it can also be used to copy one byte of data from a memory location whose address is specified by the H,L registers to a register within the CPU or *vice versa*. The form of this instruction for the movement between registers is:

```
Opcode  Operand
MOV     reg 1,reg 2
```

Examples:

```
MOV     E,B             ;copy the contents of reg
                        ;B into reg E
MOV     A,E             ;copy the contents of reg
                        ;E into the accumulator
```

For movement from memory the form is:

Opcode   Operand
MOV   reg,M

This instruction loads a specified register with the contents of the memory location whose address is given by the contents of the H,L register.

Examples:

```
MOV     A,M             ;load acc from memory
MOV     D,M             ;load D reg from memory
```

The form of the instruction for a transfer to memory is:

Opcode   Operand
MOV   M,reg

Example:

```
MOV     M,A             ;store the content of
                        ;accumulator in memory
```

Again the memory location's address is stored in the H,L registers.

In all of these examples the contents of the source register are unaffected because the MOV instruction implies a copying process.

Figure 9.3 shows a segment of a program using MVI and MOV instructions. Examine it for a while and try to work out the contents of memory location 0410 (hex) at the end of the program. I have left the comments out to make it more difficult.

The answer is, of course, 11111111, or FF (hex). The first two MVI instructions load H and L with the address 0410 (hex). Then register B is loaded with FF (hex) copied into the accumulator with the first

Label	Opcode	Operand	Comment
	MVI	H,04H	
	MVI	L,10H	
	MVI	B,11111111B	
	MOV	A,B	
	MOV	M,A	

Figure 9.3

MOV instruction and then the accumulator is copied into the memory location.

An important point to note is that at the end of the program the contents of the accumulator and the B register are also FF (hex). This is because the MOV instruction *copies* and does not physically move the binary word.

The DCR instruction

This mnemonic is short for DeCrement Register. The instruction subtracts one from the contents of the specified register. The form of the instruction is

```
Opcode   Operand
DCR      reg
```

The register can be any register: A,B,C,D,E,H or L. For example:

```
DCR      A              ;subtract 1 from acc
```

Also this instruction can be used to subtract one from the *contents* of a memory location whose address is given by the contents of the H and L registers. For example:

```
DCR      M              ;subtract 1 from memory
                        ;location given by H,L
```

The process of decrementing a register may also effect the flag register. In particular if the result of the decrement is zero the bit within the flag register indicating zero result will be set to 'one'.

As I shall show later this is a useful feature which enables more complex programs than the one considered up until now.

The INX instruction

This INcrement register pair instruction adds 'one' to the contents of a register pair. For example if the H,L pair contained

0011000011110000

before the instruction, its contents would be

0011000011110001

after the instruction.

The form of the instruction is

```
Opcode   Operand
INX      reg pair
```

The first letter of the pair is used to designate which registers are involved. For example:

```
INX      H                 ;add 1 to H,L
INX      D                 ;add 1 to D,E
```

I will use this instruction in an example later.

The JNZ instruction

This Jump if Not Zero instruction tests the setting of the zero flag. It has the form

```
Opcode    Operand
JNZ       address
```

If the zero flag is zero, which indicates that the result of the preceding operations was not zero, the next instruction which is executed is that at the address given in the operand. This address will be of an instruction in some other part of the ROM corresponding to an instruction in another part of the program.

If the zero flag is 'one', which indicates that the result of the previous operations was zero, the next instruction to be executed will be that following the JNZ instruction. For example:

```
DCR      A                 ;decrement accumulator
JNZ      0410H             ;if acc ≠ 0 jump to 0410H
MOV      B,A               ;copy acc to B reg
```

The first instruction subtracts 'one' from the accumulator, the next tests to see if the result is zero. If it is, the next instruction executed is MOV B,A; if not the next instruction executed is located at memory location 0410H. The program then continues from that location.

Because the programming examples are getting more complex I want to introduce a graphical technique to help explain and document these examples. This technique is the use of flow charts. Figure 9.4 shows a flow chart representation of this latest example using the JNZ instruction. Notice that ordinary instructions are shown as rectangular boxes with one line entering and one line leaving. Instructions that involve a decision based on a test are represented by a parallelogram with one line entering and two leaving. The flow diagram therefore shows clearly the way in which a test instruction can be used to change the flow of a program. Such a change is often referred to as a *program branch* and instructions of the same type as JNZ are called *branching instructions*.

The use of branching instructions poses several problems to the programmers. The main one is: How can they know the address of the memory location that the program control should jump to before the program has been finished and assembled into machine code?

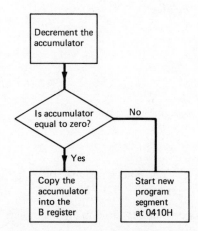

Figure 9.4 Flow diagram illustrating the effect of a JNZ instruction

One method that the programmer can use is to determine from the manufacturer's literature the number of memory locations each instruction will take. Starting from the beginning it is possible, but not easy, to calculate the expected address of the instruction to which the program should jump.

A much better method is to use a label or symbol instead of the address. The following example helps to explain this method:

Label	Opcode	Operand	Comment
	MOV	A,M	;copy memory location into A
	DCR	A	
	JNZ	TEST	;jump to TEST if A ≠ 0
	CMA		
	MOV	M,A	
TEST:	MVI	H,41H	

Notice that this example uses for the first time a label in the label field.

The label makes it easy for the programmer to specify the address of the jump instruction; it is just the label which is given to the instruction line the programmer wants the program to branch too.

As I have said before labels are optional but in the example you should be able to see their value. The assembler program which converts the source program, such as that in the example, to binary patterns will automatically generate the correct address for the label.

The label is therefore treated as having the value of the memory location where the instruction it is associated with is assembled.

Suppose the following instructions were located in the given memory locations after assembly:

Memory location (hex)	Label	Opcode	Operand	Comment
01FF		JNZ	START	
.				
.				
.				
.				
02FF	START:	DCR	A	

What is the value of the label START? The label is assigned the value of the instruction it is labelling, therefore it is 02FFH.

The rules for the number of letters or numbers used in an assembler vary, but the following are typical:

1   A label can be six characters long.

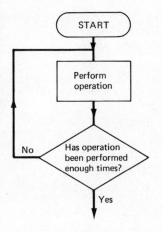

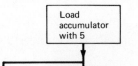

Figure 9.5 Flow diagram for a 'loop'

2 The label must terminate with a colon.
3 A label can only be associated with one label field but it can appear in the operand field of several instructions, such as JNZ in the example above.

9.4 Program loops

Program loops are one of the most useful programming techniques and as I have now introduced enough instructions for you to understand how such loops can be formed, this is a good time to go into some detail on such loops.

Figure 9.5 shows a flow diagram of a program loop. In this flow diagram a certain operation is performed a number of times before the program proceeds. If the required number of operations has not been implemented the program loops back; if it has the program continues to further instructions.

One of the simplest, but most useful, examples of a loop can be implemented using the JNZ, DCR and MVI instructions, for example:

```
        MVI     A,05H       ;load acc with 05 hex
                            ;(5 denary)
LOOP:   DCR     A           ;decrement acc by 1
        JNZ     LOOP        ;if acc ≠ 0 jump to LOOP
```

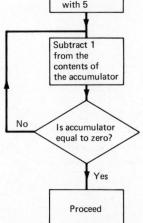

The detailed flow diagram for this program is shown in Figure 9.6. The basic operation of the program is to decrement the accumulator five times before passing on to the rest of the main program. You may well be thinking that this is a pretty pointless exercise for the processor. At first sight it seems so, but this loop can be used for timing purposes. It is possible, using manufacturers' data of the type in the Appendix, to predict exactly how long the processor takes to complete one loop. The total delay produced, before the program moves on, is five times this basic delay.

Delay loops are often important techniques used when interfacing to, for example, interface devices such as analogue-to-digital converters. For instance, there may well be a requirement for the processor to signal the converter to begin its convertion and then *wait* a fixed time before reading the data from the converter.

Figure 9.6 Detailed flow diagram for a 'loop'

Another example of a programming loop is shown below:

```
          MVI     A,05H        ;load accumulator with
                               ;05 hex
          MVI     H,01H        ;load H,L memory
          MVI     L,00H        ;addressing register with
                               ;0100 hex
                               ;blank comment line for
                               ;clarity
LOOP:     MVI     M,00H        ;move 00 hex to the memory
                               ;location given by H,L
          INX     H,           ;add 1 to the contents of
                               ;the H,L pair
          DCR     A
          JNZ     LOOP         ;acc≠0 jump to LOOP
```

Its flow diagram is shown in Figure 9.7. This program places 00 (hex) in five consecutive memory locations starting at 0100 (hex) before proceeding.

How could the above program be modified so that it filled 15 memory locations with 00 (hex), starting at 0100 (hex)? Answer: by loading the accumulator initially with 0F (hex), i.e. 15 (denary). Program loops

Q9.3   are therefore a neat way of performing repetitive tasks.

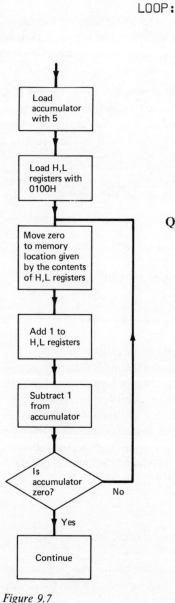

Figure 9.7

9.5   Input and output instructions

These instructions are the ones that are used to input data from a peripheral and to output data to a peripheral. The form of the instruction is:

Opcode	Operand	Comment
IN	number	;input instruction
OUT	number	;output instruction

The number in the operand field is the number of the peripheral. For the 8080 it must be in the range 0–255. Different peripherals have different numbers associated with them. Usually there is just one number for each peripheral but more complex peripherals require more.

The IN and OUT instructions affect the accumulator and the specified peripheral. For example the instruction:

```
IN        100              ;input data from peripheral
                           ;100 via data bus
```

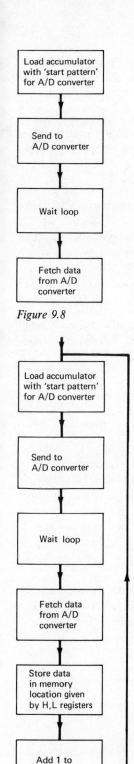

Figure 9.8

takes an 8-bit word of data from peripheral 100 and stores it in the accumulator:

```
OUT        101             ;output data to peripheral
                           ;101 via data bus
```

This instruction copies the current contents of the accumulator to the peripheral number 101.

Both IN and OUT instructions use the data bus for the transfers. Exactly how a peripheral recognises that the data is meant for it is beyond the scope of this book and indeed from the point of view of the programmer it is largely irrelevant.

An example of the use of the IN/OUT instructions and a program loop could be the following program example associated with an analogue-to-digital converter:

```
       MVI    A,00000001B  ;load accumulator
       OUT    1            ;output contents of acc
                           ;to device controlling
                           ;A/D
       MVI    A,10H        ;load acc with 10 hex
LOOP:  DCR    A            ;waiting loop
       JNZ    LOOP
       IN     2            ;move result of the
                           ;conversion to the acc
       MOV    M,A          ;copy acc to memory
```

The flow diagram for this program is shown in Figure 9.8.

It is possible and often useful to use loops within loops as shown in the modified flow diagram of Figure 9.9 and the following modified example:

```
LOOP2: MVI    A,00000001B
       OUT    1
       MVI    A,10H
LOOP1: DCR    A
       JNZ    LOOP1
       MOV    M,A
       IN     2            ;move data to acc
       INX    H            ;add 1 to H,L
                           ;this has the effect of
                           ;storing the next data in
                           ;the next memory location
       JMP    LOOP2        ;return to beginning (LOOP2)
```

Figure 9.9 Flow diagram for a program that uses a loop within a loop

There is one new instruction in this program segment; this is JMP. This is called an unconditional jump instruction. Its effect is to cause the program to always jump back to LOOP2.

The overall effect of this program is to fill successive memory locations with the results of the A/D conversion. Without any further modification this program would, of course, fill all of the available memory.

Other microprocessors use different methods of performing input and output instructions. Perhaps the most common alternative method is one called *'memory-mapped input and output'*. In this method peripheral devices are constructed with control logic which makes them appear to have a particular memory address (one which is not being used by the processor for RAM or ROM). This means that all of the instructions relating to memory locations can be used as input and output instructions, which allows a greater flexibility.

Q9.2 Memory-mapped input/output is the only form of input and output instruction allowed on the Motorola 6800 family of micro-processors.

9.6   Subroutine calls

This is the final programming technique that I want to consider in this chapter.

When a particular group of instructions, such as the examples in this chapter, is required several times in a program it is wasteful to include the full group of instructions each time. Instead the required group is written only once and when it is required again all that is necessary is to call it using the CALL instruction. The form of this instruction is:

Opcode   *Operand*
CALL   address

The address is the memory location where the first instruction in the required program segment is stored. Usually this will be a label. For example suppose the program segment required is:

```
TIME:    MVI    A,05H
LOOP:    DCR    A
         JNZ    A
```

then each time the instruction

```
CALL     TIME
```

is encountered the processor will perform this delay loop. Program segments used repeatedly in this way are called *subroutines*.

Another instruction is vital to the proper use of subroutines. This is the RET instruction. The RETurn instruction ensures that the processor returns, on completion of the subroutine, to the instruction following the CALL instruction.

Therefore, each subroutine should begin with a label and end with a RET instruction. For example the subroutine

```
TIME:    MVI    A,05H
LOOP:    DCR    A
         JNZ    LOOP
         RET
```

would return the processor to the correct instruction.

In general the subroutine will alter the contents of the registers in the processor. For example, the DCR instruction in the example alters the contents by the accumulator. This means that any data in the accumulator must be stored somewhere in the RAM before the subroutine begins to use the register or it will be lost.

Often all of the contents of the accumulator and B,C,D,E,H and L registers may need to be stored and then recalled before return from the subroutine.

The instructions used to store and retrieve data are PUSH and POP. The form of the instructions are

```
Opcode    Operand
PUSH      register pair
POP       register pair
```

The PUSH instruction stores 16 bits at a time so the pair could be the accumulator and status (flag) registers referred to in the operand as PSW, the B and C registers are referred to as B, the D and E registers are referred to as D, or the H and L registers referred to as H. Similarly the POP instruction recalls the registers in pairs. The timing loop subroutine example described before should, if all the registers are to be saved for later use, have the form

```
TIME:    PUSH   PSW         ;save accumulator plus
                            ;status
         PUSH   B           ;save B & C
         PUSH   D           ;save D & E
         PUSH   H           ;save H & L
         MVI    A,05H
LOOP:    DCR    A
         JNZ    LOOP
         POP    H           ;recall H & L
         POP    D           ;recall D & E
         POP    B           ;recall B & C
         POP    PSW         ;recall accumulator plus
                            ;status
         RET
```

This example illustrates one important rule that the programmer must follow. *This is that those registers which are first to be stored with the PUSH instruction must be last to be recalled with the POP instruction.*

The special area within the memory which is used as this special temporary storage area is called the *stack*.

You may be wondering how the processors keep track of exactly where the contents of various registers are stored. It does this using a register which I referred to when I described the microprocessor model earlier. This register is called the *stack pointer*.

Exactly how the stack pointer is used need not concern us here. However, it is important to remember the following rules:

1 Subroutines are called using a CALL instruction.
2 The last instruction in a subroutine should be RET.
3 The first instructions in a subroutine must store the contents of the registers the subroutine will use by means of PUSH instructions.
4 Before the RET instruction the contents of the registers must be recalled using POP instructions.
5 The first registers to be stored must be the last to be recalled.

9.7   Discussion

This has been a long and detailed chapter and I am sure at times it may have appeared to be just a list of 'programming tricks'. However, I feel sure that as you study the next chapter and continue your study of microprocessors beyond this book you will realise that the ideas introduced in this chapter form a sound basis for a full understanding
Q9.1, 9.4   of microprocessor programming.

9.8   Summary

1 The five main types of microprocessor instruction are:
   a Data movement instruction such as MOV and MVI.
   b Input and output instructions such as IN and OUT.
   c Arithmetic instructions such as DCR.
   d Logical instructions.
   e Test and Jump instructions such as JNZ.

2 A line of assembler program has four fields: *label*, *opcode*, *operand* and *comment*.

3 The fields are separated by delimiters: a label is ended by : , opcode and operand are separated by spaces and a comment is begun ; .

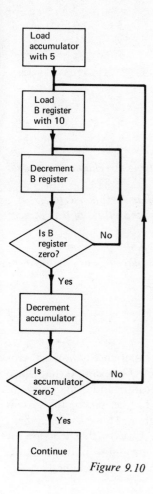

Figure 9.10

4 Jump instructions can be used along with the appropriate label to form programming loops.

5 Flow diagrams are a useful diagrammatical way of describing the operation of complex programs.

6 Subroutines can be used if the program requires the same set of operations to be performed many times.

Questions

9.1 Write down a line of an assembler program, including comments, for the following:
a Load the accumulator with 20 (hex).
b Copy the contents of the accumulator to the B register.
c Copy the contents of the B register into the memory location given by the contents of the H,L registers.
d Copy the contents of the memory location whose address is given by the H,L register pair into the C register.
e Decrement the accumulator.
f Increment the H,L registers.

9.2 Sketch a flow diagram for a segment of program which inputs some data from an interface device, waits in a delay loop and then outputs the data to another interface device.

9.3 Write a program segment that will place 11 (hex) in five successive memory locations.

9.4 Write a program that obeys the flow diagram shown in Figure 9.10.

Chapter 10 **Programming example**

Objectives *When you have completed studying this chapter you should be able to:*
1 *Write a segment of program to control an A/D converter.*
2 *Write a segment of program to linearise the output of a non-linear transducer.*
3 *Perform small modifications to an assembler program.*
4 *Arrange binary data so that it may be displayed on a seven-segment display.*

The aim of this chapter is to give you some experience of how a microprocessor can be used in a practical situation. The example that I have chosen to describe is a temperature monitoring and display system. We are not in a position to produce a full design for the system because that would require a circuit diagram. However using ideas introduced earlier we can produce a perfectly workable program for the processor. Moreover the techniques introduced in this example are applicable to a wide range of microprocessor systems.

10.1 Specification of the temperature and display system

A block diagram of the proposed system is shown in Figure 10.1. The input to the system is a temperature transducer and its associated A/D convertor. A two-digit display is the output from the system. The microprocessor controls the A/D convertor and the display. The operation of the device is to be automatic so no operator interface is required.

System specification

Temperature range	0–50°C
Temperature transducer	A thermistor
Frequency of temperature measurement	Approximately once a second
Accuracy	2% (but see later discussion)
A/D and display systems	To be discussed later

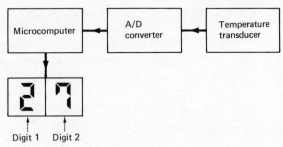

Figure 10.1 Block diagram of a temperature display system

At first sight this seems a simple system but as you will see as we begin to examine it in more detail, there is more to it than meets the eye.

Before any program is written for a microprocessor it is important to examine the various parts of the system in some detail and this example is no exception.

10.2 System elements to be used

The temperature transducer

A thermistor is a semiconductor device whose resistance varies considerably with temperature. Figure 10.2 shows a graph of this variation for a typical thermistor. The resistance of the thermistor decreases with temperature and moreover this change in resistance is not linearily related to temperature. Table 10.1 shows this variation in resistance for the thermistor used in our example.

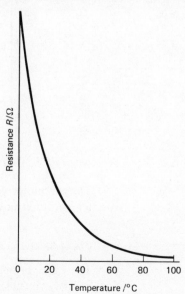

Figure 10.2 Variation of resistance with temperature for a thermistor

Table 10.1

Temperature/°C	Resistance/Ω
0	355,000
25	100,000
50	34,000
100	6,000

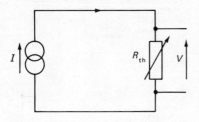

Figure 10.3   Temperature transducer circuit

I will show you later how the microprocessor can cope with this non-linear variation but first this resistance variation must be changed into a voltage variation so that it can be handled by the A/D convertor. The way to do this is put the thermistor in a circuit such as is shown in Figure 10.3. The constant current source, $\ominus$, supplies a fixed steady current. The voltage across the thermistor, V, obeys the equation known as Ohms relationship, $V = IR_{th}$, where I is the current from the constant-current generator and R_{th} is the resistance of the thermistor.

What happens to the voltage V if the temperature of the thermistor falls? The fall in temperature *increases* the resistance of the thermistor so as I is constant the voltage V must increase. The value of I can be chosen to ensure that the output voltage across the thermistor at 0°C is 15 V. If this constant current is chosen, Table 10.2 and Figure 10.4 show the voltage that would be obtained at other temperatures.

Table 10.2

Temperature/°C	Voltage/V
0	15.00
25	4.23
50	1.44
100	0.25

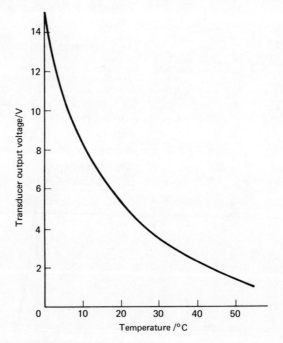

Figure 10.4   Output voltage versus temperature for transducer circuit

The circuit of Figure 10.3 is therefore going to be used for our temperature measurement.

The A/D converter

There are various types of A/D converters but I shall choose one with a fairly typical specification. Two of the most important parameters of an A/D converter are its *conversion time*, the time taken to convert an analogue voltage into its equivalent binary number, and the number of bits used in this number.

Most 8-bit microprocessors will use 8-bit A/D converters; these can represent 256 different levels so such converters can represent analogue voltage with an error of less than 1%. This is usually sufficient for most general-purpose data-logging applications and would be fine for our purpose too. However, for the purposes of keeping the explanation clear I will consider a 4-bit A/D converter (but all of my arguments will hold for 8-bit converters).

The conversion time of the A/D convertor in my example I will take to be 1 ms. This is fairly typical for a low speed and fairly cheap (less than £10) converter.

Figure 10.5 shows a block diagram of this typical converter. The conversion is started by a voltage representing a 'one' being applied to the INITIATE CONVERSION connection to the A/D converter. A millisecond later the 4 binary bits representing the analogue input information appear as voltages on the output lines. Often, as mentioned earlier, the converter signals the processor using another wire, to indicate the exact moment the output is available, but that signal is not necessary for our simple system.

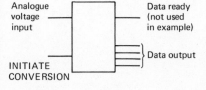

Figure 10.5 A 4-bit A/D convertor

The display subsystem

The display subsystem is to be of the seven-segment type shown in Figure 10.6. Seven light-emitting bars can be lit in patterns which can represent the digits 0–9. In addition these displays quite often have a decimal point 'dot' as shown.

Each of the seven segments plus the decimal point can be controlled on/off by the eight bits of a binary word. If the binary word is applied to the segments as shown in Figure 10.7 such that a 'one' turns a

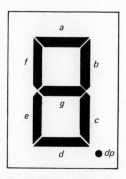

Figure 10.6   A seven-segment display including the labels for the segments and the decimal point

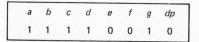

a	b	c	d	e	f	g	dp
1	1	1	1	0	0	1	0

Figure 10.7 Examples of a binary pattern control for a seven-segment display

segment on, what would be the number displayed? The number would be three ⅃ . Table 10.3 shows the binary patterns required for each of the numbers 0 to 9.

Table 10.3

Number displayed	Appearance	Binary pattern a b c d e f g (dp)
0		1 1 1 1 1 1 0 0
1		0 1 1 0 0 0 0 0
2		1 1 0 1 1 0 1 0
3		1 1 1 1 0 0 1 0
4		0 1 1 0 0 1 1 0
5		1 0 1 1 0 1 1 0
6		1 0 1 1 1 1 1 0
7		1 1 1 0 0 0 1 0 0
8		1 1 1 1 1 1 1 0
9		1 1 1 1 0 1 1 0

The system under consideration requires a two-digit display. Therefore, two binary words must be sent to the display, one for each digit, every time it is updated. The specification states that this must be every second.

The microprocessor

For the purpose of this example we will use an 8080 type processor, although virtually any other 8-bit machine would be as good. This processor also requires RAM and ROM to be associated with it, the RAM for temporary storage and the ROM for program storage.

10.3 Flow diagram for the program

Once the various subsystems have been decided upon and their specification studied the only task remaining is to write the program. For this example we will use assembler statements but for other more complex programs it may be more appropriate to use a high-level language.

Before the detailed programming is started it is important to specify what the program is to do, much in the same way that it was necessary to specify the subsystems. One of the best ways to specify the program is to use a flow diagram. This need not be too detailed at first but as the program is developed it should become more detailed.

Figure 10.8 shows a preliminary flow diagram for our system. It is a fairly simple flow diagram and you should have some idea how to program some of the functions in the boxes. For instance, signalling the A/D counter to begin and sending codes to the displays would require some form of OUT instruction, whilst receiving the data from the A/D convertor requires an IN instruction. The 1.5 ms wait can be achieved with a wait loop and a repetitive nature of the program ensured with a jump (JMP) instruction back to the beginning, as shown on the flow diagram.

The 1 second delay before the JMP statement ensures that the display is updated approximately once a second. In reality, to achieve an update at exactly one-second intervals, this large delay needs to be somewhat less than a second as the rest of the program takes some time to execute.

Two program segments will require techniques that we have not considered specifically up to now.

To develop the program in detail let us consider each of the boxes in the flow diagram in turn.

10.4 The program segments

One important point that I must stress before I begin to write this program is that my program will certainly not be the best way to implement the temperature system. This is largely because I have chosen to introduce only a few of the many instructions available to the programmer, so that I can keep this introduction to programming as clear as possible. However the program that results will work provided the hardware of the system is as I have described it earlier in this chapter.

The start segment

When a microprocessor system is switched on the processor performs

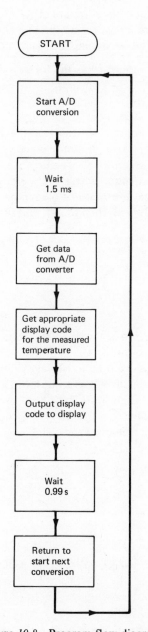

Figure 10.8 Program flow diagram

a series of checks and operations to test that it is fit to begin the program stored in its memory. These checks are automatic and the processor begins to carry out the program at the first memory location of the program. The program may be placed anywhere in memory by the assembler so the programmer must ensure that the assembler produces machine code starting at the expected location. This is done by the use of a special assembler facility called an assembler directive. These directives look like program instructions, but they do not form part of the program proper; instead they direct the operation of the assembler when it is producing the binary code.

The directive that concerns us at the moment has the form:

Opcode	*Operand*
ORG	address

This is usually the first line of any program. In this line the programmer directs the assembler to produce program code which begins at the address specified. The assembler also ensures that the processor, when it has completed its initial checks, goes to this address for its first instruction. If we assume that in our example the ROM area of memory begins at 2000 (hex), then this should be the address in our ORG statement:

Opcode	*Operand*	*Comment*
ORG	2000H	;start program at 2000 (hex)

Conversion request signal

All that is required to start the conversion is a 'one' to be applied to the INITIATE CONVERSION connection on the A/D convertor. The OUT instruction outputs eight bits at a time so we have a choice as to which of these bits is used for the conversion request. To keep things simple, let us choose the least significant bit. The control circuitry associated with the A/D convertor is arranged to begin conversion whenever a word is sent to it from the processor which has its least significant bit equal to 1.

The required program instructions are therefore:

Opcode	*Operand*	*Comment*
MVI	A,01H	;load accumulator with
		;00000001
OUT	1	;send request to A/D

Notice that I have called the A/D control circuitry output device 1.

The 1.5 ms wait loop

This loop will have the same form as those we considered earlier:

```
              MVI       A,05H          ;load accumulator with 5
LOOP:         DCR       A              ;decrement accumulator
              JNZ       LOOP           ;if accumulator is 0 jump
                                       ;to loop
```

The loop is executed five times before the processor proceeds. To find how much time this takes we need to use the Appendix. From the Appendix:

DCR takes five time periods

JNZ takes ten time periods

MVI A,05H takes seven time periods

Once round the loop therefore takes fifteen time periods. The loop is performed five times so the total delay from this piece of program is 5 × 15 plus 7 from the MVI instruction. The total is therefore 82 time periods. The time period depends on the frequency of the clock used to control the processor but a fairly typical value is one microsecond (10^{-6} s). Using this value gives a delay of

$$82 \times 10^{-6} \text{ s}$$

What is the maximum delay that could be achieved with this simple loop? The maximum number that can be loaded into the accumulator is 255 and this would give a total delay of $(255 \times 15) + 7 = 3,832$ µs. This is approximately equal to 3.8 ms.

A delay of 1.5 ms can be achieved by loading 100 into the accumulator. The required program segment is therefore:

```
              MVI       A,64H          ;load accumulator with 100
LOOP:         DCR       A
              JNZ       LOOP
```

The 1.0 s wait loop

The maximum delay that can be achieved by the simple delay loop described in the previous section is 3.8 ms, so a one second delay requires the basic loop to be modified. This is done by two delay loops, one within the other. One of the loops gives the maximum delay of 3.8 ms and the other loop ensures that the 3.8 ms loop is performed 255 times. Because most of the time is wasted by the instructions in the 3.8 ms loop the total delay is $255 \times 3.8 \text{ ms} = 0.97$ s. The required program segment is:

```
              MVI       B,0FFH         ;load reg B with 255
LOOP2:        MVI       A,0FFH         ;load accumulator with 255
LOOP1:        DCR       A              ;loop1 gives 3.8 ms delay
              JNZ       LOOP1
              DCR       B              ;decrement B reg
              JNZ       LOOP2          ;if B≠0 repeat loop2
```

The original specification for the system required an update of the temperature approximately once a second. The combination of the 1.5 ms and 0.97 s each time the program completes a cycle around the flow diagram will ensure this, plus the delays from other instructions.

Receiving data from the A/D convertor

As I mentioned earlier, the A/D convertor would normally supply 8 bits of data at the end of a conversion, but to keep the next program segments simple I will assume that there are only 4 bits. Furthermore I will assume that they are sent from the converter as the four least most significant digits of an 8-bit word and the most significant four are set to zero. The required program segment is:

```
IN       2              ;device 2 is chosen to be
                        ;output of A/D
```

This line of program places the result of the A/D conversion in the four least significant digits of the accumulator.

Segment relating A/D convertor output to the codes to be sent to the display

This segment performs two functions: it relates the code from the A/D convertor to the temperature and it produces the pattern of ones and zeros that enables this temperature to be displayed on the two seven-segment displays.

Remember that for simplicity I am only considering a four-digit conversion and that a 4-digit binary number can only represent 16 different voltages exactly. Figure 10.9 shows the voltage out of the transducer related to temperature; also shown are the voltage levels that can be represented exactly by the 4-digit binary number. With just 4 digits there are large gaps between these voltage levels so it is inevitable that with the 4-bit system there will be large errors.

How many voltage levels can be represented by 8 binary digits? Answer – 256. Even with 8 bits it will not be possible to represent all the voltage levels, but the error will be considerably smaller.

Table 10.4 shows the relation between temperature, transducer voltage output and the code produced by the A/D convertor. Notice that by choosing 15 V to be the maximum voltage gives a simple relation between the binary code and the voltage. The binary code for 15 represents 15 V and so on.

Once this code is received by the processor it must be related to the patterns required for the seven-segment display. Table 10.5 shows the required patterns for each of the codes from the A/D convertor and

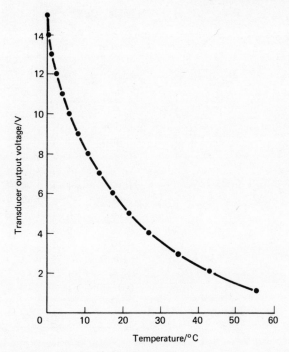

Figure 10.9 Voltages on the voltage/temperature curve which can be represented exactly by a 4-bit binary code

Table 10.4

Transducer output/V	Temperature/°C	Binary code
15	0	1111
14	1	1110
13	2	1101
12	3	1100
11	4	1011
10	6	1010
9	8	1001
8	11	1000
7	14	0111
6	12.5	0110
5	22	0101
4	27	0100
3	35	0011
2	44	0010
1	56	0001

Table 10.5

Code from A/D converter	Output to display																Displayed temperature
	Digit 1								Digit 2								
	a	b	c	d	f	e	g	dp	a	b	c	d	e	f	g	dp	
1111	1	1	1	1	1	1	0	0	1	1	1	1	1	1	0	0	00
1110	1	1	1	1	1	1	0	0	0	1	1	0	0	0	0	0	01
1101	1	1	1	1	1	1	0	0	1	1	0	1	1	0	1	0	02
1100	1	1	1	1	1	1	0	0	1	1	1	1	0	0	1	0	03
1011	1	1	1	1	1	1	0	0	0	1	1	0	0	1	1	0	04
1010	1	1	1	1	1	1	0	0	1	0	1	1	1	1	1	0	06
1001	1	1	1	1	1	1	0	0	1	1	1	1	1	1	1	0	08
1000	0	1	1	0	0	0	0	0	0	1	1	0	0	0	0	0	11
0111	0	1	1	0	0	0	0	0	0	1	1	0	0	1	1	0	14
0110	0	1	1	0	0	0	0	0	1	1	1	1	1	1	1	0	18
0101	1	1	0	1	1	0	1	0	1	1	0	1	1	0	1	0	22
0100	1	1	0	1	1	0	1	0	1	1	1	0	0	1	0	0	27
0011	1	1	1	1	0	0	1	0	1	0	1	1	0	1	1	0	35
0010	0	1	1	0	0	1	1	0	0	1	1	0	0	1	1	0	44
0001	1	0	1	1	0	1	1	0	1	0	1	1	1	1	1	0	56

Table 10.6

Address (hex)	Contents Digit 1	Address (hex)	Contents Digit 2
1000	?	1010	?
1001	10110110	1011	10111110
1002	01100110	1012	01100110
1003	11110010	1013	10110110
1004	11011010	1014	11100100
1005	11011010	1015	11011010
1006	01100000	1016	11111110
1007	01100000	1017	01100110
1008	01100000	1018	01100000
1009	11111100	1019	11111110
100A	11111100	101A	10111110
100B	11111100	101B	01100110
100C	11111100	101C	11110010
100D	11111100	101D	11011010
100E	11111100	101E	01100000
100F	11111100	101F	11111100

as I explained in above these patterns will produce recognisable numerals from the displays.

For this program segment to work correctly the information relating the codes from the A/D convertor to the patterns for the displays

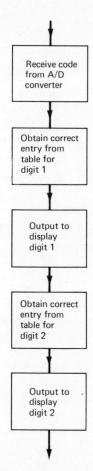

Figure 10.10 Flow diagram for program segment relating A/D codes and required display

Figure 10.11

must be stored in the memory of the microcomputer. There are assembler directives which enable this to be done fairly easily so I want you to assume that the information in Table 10.5 is available in memory. Moreover, it is stored in two separate areas, one for each digit as shown in Table 10.6. Notice that I have left the first memory location blank as I shall be returning to consider what should be its contents in a question at the end of this chapter.

However, the most important thing to notice is that I have arranged that the contents of the tables in memory are inverted versions of Table 10.5. That is to say the patterns for digit 1 and 2 corresponding to the A/D code 0001 appear at the top of the memory list, the patterns for 0010 are 2 down, etc. Hopefully you will soon see the reason for this.

Figure 10.10 shows a detailed flow diagram for this program segment which relates A/D codes to display patterns.

The code from the A/D convertor is to be used to obtain two entries from the memory. Initially the code will be stored in the accumulator but the accumulator is also used to output the pattern to the display before the second pattern is sent to the second digit. This means that the code from the A/D convertor needs to be transferred to another register to free the accumulator for the output instructions.

The instruction that can be used is MOV and it will have the form:

```
MOV      C,A          ;transfer contents of
                      ;accumulator to C reg
```

Later I will be using the B and C registers as a pair, the B reg as the most significant. Furthermore I will need the B register to contain all zeros. You will see why later. The instruction to do this is MVI; the program line will be:

```
MVI      B,00H        ;load B with zero
```

Figure 10.11 shows the effect this has on the flow diagram for this segment.

The next step is to obtain the correct pattern from the tables in memory. You should remember that the instruction used to obtain data from memory is also MOV, but with the form:

```
MOV      A,M          ;copy data in memory
                      ;location whose address is
                      ;contained in the H,L reg
                      ;to the accumulator
```

All that the program has to ensure is that the correct address is in the H,L registers before the MOV instruction is implemented. Because of the way in which the tables are organised in memory this is quite

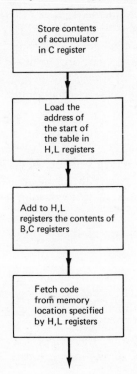

Figure 10.12   Detailed flow diagram

simple to arrange. The procedure is illustrated on the even more detailed flow diagram shown in Figure 10.12.

By reference to Table 10.6 you should be able to see that the start address for the table for digit 1 is 1000 (hex) whilst for the table for digit 2 it is 1010 (hex). These addresses can be loaded into the H,L registers using MVI instructions. For example the start address for digit 1 can be loaded as follows:

```
MVI     L,00H          ;load least significant 8
                       ;bits into L
MVI     H,10H          ;load most significant 8
                       ;bits into H
```

Note: There is an instruction which loads 16 bits at a time but in the interests of simplicity I have decided to stick with the instructions introduced earlier.

To obtain the correct pattern corresponding to the code from the A/D converter all that is required is to add the code to the start address of the table. You should be able to convince yourself that this is true by looking back at Table 10.6. If the code from the A/D has the value 1, the correct pattern is one away from the start address. Similarly if the code is 2 the correct pattern is two away and so on. The correct address is therefore obtained by adding the code to the base or start address. This addition can be performed by an instruction that I have not mentioned so far. This is the DAD instruction. It has the form:

```
DAD     reg pair
```

Its effect is to add the contents of the register pair specified to the H,L register pair. The register pair is specified by the letter of the most significant register, e.g. B means B,C and D means D,E. Our example requires B,C to be added to the H,L registers so the instruction will be:

```
DAD     B              ;add value of code now
                       ;stored in B,C to start of
                       ;the table address in H,L
```

We now have all of the information and techniques to start writing this segment of the program but before we start it is a good idea to draw one more flow diagram to check that the procedure will work. This is shown in Figure 10.13.

The full program segment is as follows:

```
MOV     C,A            ;store code from A/D in
                       ;reg C
MVI     B,00H          ;ensure B reg contains zero
MVI     L,00H          ;load the starting address
MVI     H,10H          ;of the table for digit 1
```

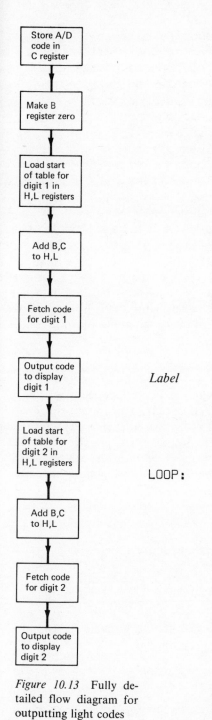

Figure 10.13 Fully detailed flow diagram for outputting light codes

```
DAD     B           ;add the code in B,C reg to
                    ;the start address
MOV     A,M         ;fetch pattern from
                    ;digit 1 table
OUT     3           ;send pattern to display 1
                    ;start the segment for
                    ;digit 2
MVI     L,10H       ;load the starting address
MVI     H,10H       ;of the table for digit 2
DAD     B           ;add the code in B,C reg to
                    ;the start address
MOV     A,M         ;fetch pattern from
                    ;digit 2 table and put it
                    ;in the accumulator
OUT     4           ;send pattern to display 2
```

This completes the individual segments and all that remains is to put all these segments together.

10.5   The complete program

Label	Opcode	Operand	Comment
	ORG	2000H	;start prog at 2000 (hex)
	MVI	A,01H	;load acc with 00000001
	OUT	1	;send request to A/D
			;1.5 ms wait
	MVI	A,64H	;load acc with 100
LOOP:	DCR	A	
	JNZ	LOOP	
			;get A/D data
	IN	2	;device 2 is chosen to be
			;output of A/D
	MOV	C,A	;store code from A/D in
			;reg C
	MVI	B,00H	;ensure B reg contains 0
	MVI	L,00H	;load the starting address
	MVI	H,10H	;of the table for digit 1
	DAD	B	;add the code in the B,C
			;reg to the start address
	MOV	A,M	;fetch pattern from digit
			;1 table
	OUT	3	;send pattern to display 1
			;start the segment for
			;digit 2
	MVI	L,10H	;load the starting address
	MVI	H,10H	;of the table for digit 2

```
              DAD    B             ;add the data in the B,C
                                   ;reg to the start address
              MOV    A,M           ;fetch pattern from digit
                                   ;2 table and put it in
                                   ;the accumulator
              OUT    4             ;send pattern to display 2
                                   ;0.99 s wait
              MVI    B,OFFH        ;load reg B with 255
     LOOP2:   MVI    A,OFFH        ;load acc with 255
     LOOP1:   DCR    A             ;loop1 gives 3.8 ms delay
              JNZ    LOOP1
              DCR    B             ;decrement B reg
              JNZ    LOOP2         ;if B ≠ 0 repeat loop2
              JMP    2000H         ;jump to start to repeat
              END
```

Notice that the final line of the program must be the assembler directive END. This tells the assembler that the end of the program has been reached and the input of the program has finished.

10.6 Discussion

The program shown in the previous section is a perfectly workable program but probably could be improved in many ways. However, my aim was to show you how, using only a few instructions, it is possible to make a microprocessor perform a practical task. In addition, the example should have shown you the advantage of splitting the program into segments and using lots of flow diagrams.

10.7 Summary

1   A microprocessor can be used to control a simple temperature-monitoring system.

2   A non-linear transducer is easily handled by a microprocessor by the use of a conversion table.

3   In this example a table was also used to generate the patterns required to drive a seven-segment display.

4   Timing loops can be used to affect the speed at which the system operates.

5   Large programs should be split up into smaller segments which are easier to handle.

6   Hardware should be specified in terms of subsystem specification and software in terms of flow diagrams.

Q10.1–10.3

Questions

10.1 I left the first address in the tables empty. What sort of temperature would cause the processor to address this location? If, when this occurs, the display is required to display ⌐‖, suggest modifications to the program which would achieve this.

10.2 Modify the program to update the display every 0.5 seconds.

10.3 Shown below is an extract from the 8080 programming manual. It describes the instructions CMP and JNC. Suggest how these instructions can be used so that the processor controls a switch when the temperature is greater than 25°C. (You will need another OUT instruction.)

CMP   COMPARE WITH ACCUMULATOR

CMP compares the specified byte with the contents of the accumulator and indicates the result by setting the carry and zero flags. The values being compared remain unchanged.

The zero flag indicates equality. No carry indicates that the accumulator is greater than the specified byte; a carry indicates that the accumulator is less than the byte. However, the meaning of the carry flag is reversed when the values have different signs or one of the values is complemented.

The program tests the condition flags using one of the conditional Jump, Call, or Return instructions. For example, JZ (Jump if Zero) tests for equality.

Functional Description:

Comparisons are performed by subtracting the specified byte from the contents of the accumulator, which is why the zero and carry flags indicate the result. This subtraction uses the processor's internal registers so that source data is preserved. Because subtraction uses two's complement addition, the CMP instruction recomplements the carry flag generated by the subtraction.

Compare Register with Accumulator

Opcode	Operand
CMP	reg

The operand must name one of the registers A through E, H or L.

1	0	1	1	1	S	S	S

Cycles: 1
States: 4
Addressing: register
Flags: Z,S,P,CY,AC

Compare Memory with Accumulator

Opcode	Operand
CMP	M

This instruction compares the contents of the memory location addressed by the H and L registers with the contents of the accumulator. M is a symbolic reference to the H and L register pair.

1	0	1	1	1	1	1	0

Cycles: 2
States: 7
Addressing: register indirect
Flags: Z,S,P,CY,AC

Example 1:

Assume that the accumulator contains the value 0AH and register E contains the value 05H. The instruction CMP E performs the following internal subtraction (remember that subtraction is actually two's complement addition):

$$
\begin{array}{lll}
\text{Accumulator} & = & 00001010 \\
+(-\text{E Register}) & = & \underline{11111011} \\
& & 00000101 \ +(-\text{carry})
\end{array}
$$

After the carry is complemented to account for the subtract operation, both the zero and carry bits are zero, thus indicating A greater than E.

Example 2:

Assume that the accumulator contains the value −1BH and register E contains 05H:

$$
\begin{array}{lll}
\text{Accumulator} & = & 11100101 \\
+(-\text{E Register}) & = & \underline{11111011} \\
& & 11100000 \ +(-\text{carry})
\end{array}
$$

After the CMP instruction recomplements the carry flag, both the carry flag and zero flag are zero. Normally this indicates that the accumulator is greater than register E. However, the meaning of the carry flag is reversed since the values have different signs. The user program is responsible for proper interpretation of the carry flag.

JUMP IF NO CARRY

The JNC instruction tests the setting of the carry flag. If there is no carry (carry flag = 0), program execution resumes at the address specified in the JNC instruction. If there is a carry (carry flag = 1), execution continues with the next sequential instruction.

Opcode	*Operand*
JNC	address

The address may be specified as a number, a label, or an expression. The assembler inverts the high and low address bytes when it assembles the instruction.

1	1	0	1	0	0	1	0
low addr								
high addr								

Cycles:	3 (2 or 3 on 8085)
States:	10 (7 or 10 on 8085)
Addressing:	immediate
Flags:	none

Appendix **Instruction summary**

This appendix summarises the bit patterns and number of time states associated with every 8080 CPU instruction. The instructions are listed in mnemonic (alphabetical) sequence. When using this summary, note the following symbols: DDD represents a destination register; SSS represents a source register. Both DDD and SSS are interpreted as follows:

DDD or SSS	Interpretation
000	Register B
001	Register C
010	Register D
011	Register E
100	Register H
101	Register L
110	A memory register or stack pointer or PSW (flags + accumulator)
111	The accumulator

Instruction execution time equals number of time periods multiplied by the duration of a time period.

A time period may vary from 480 ns to 2 μs on the 8080 or 320 ns to 2 μs on the 8085. Where two numbers of time periods are shown, it means that the smaller number of time periods is required if a condition is not met, and the larger number of time periods is required if the condition is met.

MNEMONIC	D7	D6	D5	D4	D3	D2	D1	D0	NUMBER OF TIME PERIODS	
									8080	8085
CALL	1	1	0	0	1	1	0	1	17	18
CC	1	1	0	1	1	1	0	0	11/17	9/18
CNC	1	1	0	1	0	1	0	0	11/17	9/18
CZ	1	1	0	0	1	1	0	0	11/17	9/18
CNZ	1	1	0	0	0	1	0	0	11/17	9/18
CP	1	1	1	1	0	1	0	0	11/17	9/18
CM	1	1	1	1	1	1	0	0	11/17	9/18
CPE	1	1	1	0	1	1	0	0	11/17	9/17
CPO	1	1	1	0	0	1	0	0	11/17	9/18
RET	1	1	0	0	1	0	0	1	10	10
RC	1	1	0	1	1	0	0	0	5/11	6/12
RNC	1	1	0	1	0	0	0	0	5/11	6/12
RZ	1	1	0	0	1	0	0	0	5/11	6/12
RNZ	1	1	0	0	0	0	0	0	5/11	6/12
RP	1	1	1	1	0	0	0	0	5/11	6/12
RM	1	1	1	1	1	0	0	0	5/11	6/12
RPE	1	1	1	0	1	0	0	0	5/11	6/12
RPO	1	1	1	0	0	0	0	0	5/11	6/12
RST	1	1	A	A	A	1	1	1	11	12
IN	1	1	0	1	1	0	1	1	10	10
OUT	1	1	0	1	0	0	1	1	10	10
LXI B	0	0	0	0	0	0	0	1	10	10
LXI D	0	0	0	1	0	0	0	1	10	10
LXI H	0	0	1	0	0	0	0	1	10	10
LXI SP	0	0	1	1	0	0	0	1	10	10
PUSH B	1	1	0	0	0	1	0	1	11	12
PUSH D	1	1	0	1	0	1	0	1	11	12
PUSH H	1	1	1	0	0	1	0	1	11	12
PUSH PSW	1	1	1	1	0	1	0	1	11	12
POP B	1	1	0	0	0	0	0	1	10	10

Instruction	States	States	b7	b6	b5	b4	b3	b2	b1	b0
POP D	10	10	1	1	0	1	0	0	0	1
POP H	10	10	1	1	1	0	0	0	0	1
POP PSW	10	10	1	1	1	1	0	0	0	1
STA	13	13	0	0	1	1	0	0	1	0
LDA	13	13	0	0	1	1	1	0	1	0
XCHG	4	4	1	1	1	0	1	0	1	1
XTHL	16	18	1	1	1	0	0	0	1	1
SPHL	6	5	1	1	1	1	1	0	0	1
PCHL	6	5	1	1	1	0	1	0	0	1
DAD B	10	10	0	0	0	0	1	0	0	1
DAD D	10	10	0	0	0	1	1	0	0	1
DAD H	10	10	0	0	1	0	1	0	0	1
DAD SP	10	10	0	0	1	1	1	0	0	1
STAX B	7	7	0	0	0	0	0	0	1	0
STAX D	7	7	0	0	0	1	0	0	1	0
LDAX B	7	7	0	0	0	0	1	0	1	0
LDAX D	7	7	0	0	0	1	1	0	1	0
INX B	6	5	0	0	0	0	0	0	1	1
INX D	6	5	0	0	0	1	0	0	1	1
INX H	6	5	0	0	1	0	0	0	1	1
INX SP	6	5	0	0	1	1	0	0	1	1
MOV r_1,r_2	4	5	0	1	D	D	D	S	S	S
MOV M,r	7	7	0	1	1	1	0	S	S	S
MOV r,M	7	7	0	1	D	D	D	1	1	0
HLT	5	7	0	1	1	1	0	1	1	0
MVI r	7	7	0	0	D	D	D	1	1	0
MVI M	10	10	0	0	1	1	0	1	1	0
INR	4	5	0	0	D	D	D	1	0	0
DCR	4	5	0	0	D	D	D	1	0	1
INR A	4	5	0	0	1	1	1	1	0	0
DCR A	4	5	0	0	1	1	1	1	0	1
INR M	10	10	0	0	1	1	0	1	0	0
DCR M	10	10	0	0	1	1	0	1	0	1
ADD r	4	4	1	0	0	0	0	S	S	S
ADC r	4	4	1	0	0	0	1	S	S	S

MNEMONIC	D7	D6	D5	D4	D3	D2	D1	D0	NUMBER OF TIME PERIODS 8080	NUMBER OF TIME PERIODS 8085
SUB r	1	0	0	1	0	S	S	S	4	4
SBB r	1	0	0	1	1	S	S	S	4	4
AND r	1	0	1	0	0	S	S	S	4	4
XRA r	1	0	1	0	1	S	S	S	4	4
ORA r	1	0	1	1	0	S	S	S	4	4
CMP r	1	0	1	1	1	S	S	S	4	4
ADD M	1	0	0	0	0	1	1	0	7	7
ADC M	1	0	0	0	1	1	1	0	7	7
SUB M	1	0	0	1	0	1	1	0	7	7
SBB M	1	0	0	1	1	1	1	0	7	7
AND M	1	0	1	0	0	1	1	0	7	7
XRA M	1	0	1	0	1	1	1	0	7	7
ORA M	1	0	1	1	0	1	1	0	7	7
CMP M	1	0	1	1	1	1	1	0	7	7
ADI	1	1	0	0	0	1	1	0	7	7
ACI	1	1	0	0	1	1	1	0	7	7
SUI	1	1	0	1	0	1	1	0	7	7
SBI	1	1	0	1	1	1	1	0	7	7
ANI	1	1	1	0	0	1	1	0	7	7
XRI	1	1	1	0	1	1	1	0	7	7
ORI	1	1	1	1	0	1	1	0	7	7
CPI	1	1	1	1	1	1	1	0	7	7
RLC	0	0	0	0	0	1	1	1	4	4
RRC	0	0	0	0	1	1	1	1	4	4
RAL	0	0	0	1	0	1	1	1	4	4
RAR	0	0	0	1	1	1	1	1	4	4
JMP	1	1	0	0	0	0	1	1	10	10
JC	1	1	0	1	1	0	1	0	10	7/10
JNC	1	1	0	1	0	0	1	0	10	7/10
JZ	1	1	0	0	1	0	1	0	10	7/10

Mnemonic										
JNZ	1	1	0	0	0	0	1	0	7/10	10
JP	1	1	1	1	0	0	1	0	7/10	10
JM	1	1	1	1	1	0	1	0	7/10	10
JPE	1	1	1	0	1	0	1	0	7/10	10
JPO	1	1	1	0	0	0	1	0	7/10	10
DCX B	0	0	0	0	1	0	1	1	6	5
DCX D	0	0	0	1	1	0	1	1	6	5
DCX H	0	0	1	0	1	0	1	1	6	5
DCX SP	0	0	1	1	1	0	1	1	6	5
CMA	0	0	1	0	1	1	1	1	4	4
STC	0	0	1	1	0	1	1	1	4	4
CMC	0	0	1	1	1	1	1	1	4	4
DAA	0	0	1	0	0	1	1	1	4	4
SHLD	0	0	1	0	0	0	1	0	16	16
LHLD	0	0	1	0	1	0	1	0	16	16
RIM	0	0	1	0	0	0	0	0	4	—
SIM	0	0	1	1	0	0	0	0	4	—
EI	1	1	1	1	1	0	1	1	4	4
DI	1	1	1	1	0	0	1	1	4	4
NOP	0	0	0	0	0	0	0	0	4	4

Answers to Questions

1.1 They are small, cheap and reliable.

1.2 *(a)* The software of the microcomputer consists of the computer programs that give the microcomputer a description of the task it is to perform and provide it with the instructions that enable it to operate.
(b) The hardware of the microcomputer consists of all the physical objects in the system, e.g. the microprocessor, the memory devices and the board the devices are mounted on.

1.3 The microprocessor uses memory to store data and to store the program. The different parts of memory are sometimes called the data store and the program store. The data store contains numbers to be processed and the program store holds the instructions that enable the microprocessor to operate.

1.4 *(a)* 1 1 0 1
$(1 \times 2^3) + (1 \times 2^2) + (0 \times 2^1) + (1 \times 2^0)$
$(1 \times 8) + (1 \times 4) + (0 \times 2) + (1 \times 1)$
$8 + 4 + 0 + 1$
13

(b) 0 0 1 0
$(0 \times 2^3) + (0 \times 2^2) + (1 \times 2^1) + (0 \times 2^0)$
$(0 \times 8) + (0 \times 4) + (1 \times 2) + (0 \times 1)$
$0 + 0 + 2 + 0$
2

(c) 11111110. This number is just one less than the maximum for an 8-bit number (255). Therefore the answer is 254.

(d) 01010101
$(0 \times 2^7) + (1 \times 2^6) + (0 \times 2^5) + (1 \times 2^4) + (0 \times 2^3) + (0 \times 2^1) + (1 \times 2^0)$
$(0 \times 128) + (1 \times 64) + (0 \times 32) + (1 \times 16) + (0 \times 8) + (1 \times 4) + (0 \times 2) + (1 \times 1)$
$0 + 64 + 16 + 4 + 1$
85

1.5 *(a)* 49 is $32(2^5) + 16(2^4) + 1(2^0)$. The 8-bit representation is therefore

$(0 \times 2^7) + (0 \times 2^6) + (1 \times 2^5) + (1 \times 2^4) + (0 \times 2^3) + (0 \times 2^2) + (0 \times 2^1) + (1 \times 2^0)$

or, in more normal form, 00110001.

(b)   139 is $128(2^7) + 8(2^3) + 2(2^1) + 1(2^0)$. The 8-bit representation is therefore

$$(1 \times 2^7) + (0 \times 2^6) + (0 \times 2^5) + (0 \times 2^4) + (1 \times 2^3) + (0 \times 2^2) + (1 \times 2^1) + (1 \times 2^0)$$

or, in more normal form, 10001011.

(c)   255 is the largest number that can be represented by an 8-bit binary code. Therefore it consists of all ones: 11111111.

1.6   *(a)*   Assembly code or machine code.

   (b)   BASIC, FORTRAN, COBOL.

1.7   Assembly language is converted to machine code using a computer program known as an assembler.

2.1   *(a)*   Microprocessor unit (CPU).

   (b)   The data memory (RAM).

   (c)   The program memory (ROM).

   (d)   The input/output section.

   (e)   Busses to transfer information.

2.2   *(a)*   The word length of the microprocessor is the number of binary digits or bits which make up a single instruction or piece of data. Most microprocessors have an 8-bit word length, e.g. 10110011.

   (b)   A byte.

2.3   The accumulator.

2.4   A RAM is a random access memory or read/write memory. Information can be both read from and written to these memories. They are usually used for storing data.

2.5   *(a)*   PROM: a programmable read only memory. These can be programmed by the manufacturer or the customer after the integrated circuit has been manufactured.

   (b)   EPROM: an erasable programmable read only memory. These can be both programmed and reprogrammed after the integrated circuit has been manufactured.

2.6   Information in the form of binary words is transferred along electrical connections known as buses. These buses are the same width as the word length used by the microprocessor.

3.1   *(a)*   Keyboard, paper tape and reader, transducer, floppy disk or cassette.

   (b)   VDU, printer, paper tape punch, transducer, floppy disk or cassette.

3.2   Binary signals are obtained when the presence or absence of holes in the tape are detected by photocells or wire brushes. These devices complete a circuit when a hole is present and break the circuit when there is no hole in the tape.

3.3   *(i)* Floppy disks; *(ii)* cassette recorder and magnetic tape.

3.4   *(a)*   A transducer is a peripheral device that can convert one form of energy into electrical energy, i.e. an electrical voltage.
(b)   A digital-to-analogue (D/A) converter is an electronic circuit that converts digital signals from the computer into the analogue signals required to drive transducers.

4.1   See Figure A.

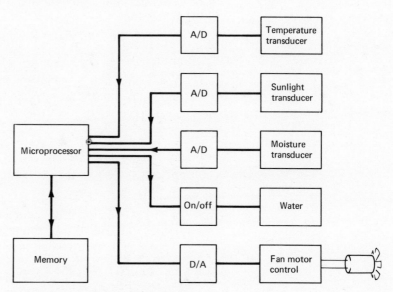

Figure A   Answer to Question 4.1

4.2   Perhaps the simplest strategy is to have two sets of reference data stored in memory: one set for temperature and one for moisture. Readings from the temperature transducer could be compared with the reference temperatures and the fan used if the temperature gets too high. Similarly if, when the data from the moisture transducer is compared with its reference data, it shows that the soil is too dry the process can switch on the sprinkler.

4.3   The problems of using polling are somewhat interrelated but basically they are that polling is
(a)   wasteful of processor time;
(b)   sometimes unable to test the A/D convertor for valid data frequently enough.

4.4 *(a)* A/D

(b) D/A

(c) None

(d) A/D

5.1 After an interrupt has been detected the processor has to:

1 Stop what it is doing.

2 Store all the data in its internal registers in the main memory.

3 Store information to enable it to return to the correct place in the program after the interrupt has been handled.

4 Determine which device has interrupted.

5 Perform the instructions required by the interrupt.

5.2 *(a)* Interrupt

(b) Polling

(c) Interrupt

6.1 A software fault is a fault in the program controlling the microprocessor. A hardware fault is a fault in the electrical circuitry of the microprocessor or its associated devices.

7.1 *(a)* Assembler.

(b) High-level language.

(c) Machine code.

7.2 *(i)* The programmer can use mnemonics, octal and hex representation; *(ii)* the assembler program checks for errors; *(iii)* program entry is easier on large machines making corrections easier as well.

7.3 *(a)* 260, 377, 000, 252 (octal)

(b) B0, FF, 00, AA (hex)

7.4 *(a)* 00001111

(b) 00010101

(c) 0110111

8.1 See Figure 8.1

8.2 Data movement instructions

Input and output instructions

Arithmetic instructions

Logical instructions

Test instructions

8.3 The stack pointer register is used to allow the programmer to use subroutines.

8.4 The program counter register is used by the processor to keep track of the memory location from which the next instruction has to be fetched.

9.1

	Opcode	Operand	Comment
(i)	MVI	A,20H	;put 20 (hex) in acc
(ii)	MOV	B,A	;copy to acc to B reg
(iii)	MOV	M,B	;copy B reg to memory ;location given by H,L regs
(iv)	MOV	C,M	;copy into C reg the data ;in the memory location ;specified by H,L regs
(v)	DCR	A	;subtract 1 from acc
(vi)	INX	H	;add 1 to H,L pair

9.2 See Figure B.

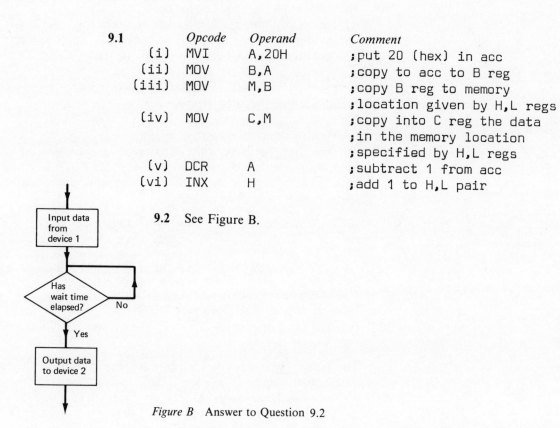

Figure B Answer to Question 9.2

9.3

Label	Opcode	Operand	Comment
	MVI	A,05H	;load acc with 5
LOOP:	MVI	M,11H	;move 11 (hex) into memory ;location given by H,L
	INX	H	;add 1 to H,L
	DCR	A	;subtract 1 from acc
	JNZ	LOOP	;acc≠0 jump to LOOP

9.4

Label	Opcode	Operand	Comment
	MVI	A,05H	;load acc with 5
LOOP1:	MVI	B,0AH	;load B with 10
LOOP2:	DCR	B	;subtract 1 from B
	JNZ	LOOP2	;B≠0 jump to LOOP2
	DCR	A	;subtract 1 from acc
	JNZ	LOOP1	;acc≠0 jump to LOOP1

10.1 Figure 10.9 shows that a low transducer output voltage which would produce 0000 from the A/D converter would correspond to a temperature very much larger than 55°C. This would be outside the specified range so the display of OL for over-limit would be appropriate. All that needs to be done to ensure this is to fill the two vacant memory locations shown in Table 10.6 with the pattern to produce OL. Therefore the contents of 1000 (hex) are

11111100

and the contents of 1010 (hex) are

00011100

10.2 This modification can be achieved by modifying the one second wait loop. Instead of loading the B register with 255 it has to be loaded with $255 \div 2 \approx 128 = 80$ (hex), the required modification is therefore to change

```
MVI      B,0FFH        ;load B reg with 255
```

to

```
MVI      B,80H         ;load B reg with 128
```

10.3 CMP must be used to compare the data from the A/D converter with some reference value stored in a register. From Table 10.4 a temperature *greater* than 25°C will be indicated by binary codes representing less than 5.

The decision to control the switch or not should be made when the data is first obtained from the A/D convertor and stored in the accumulator. The contents of the accumulator can be compared with the binary pattern for 5 stored in the E register at the start of the program with a MVI instruction, using CMP in a statement:

Opcode	*Operand*	*Comment*
CMP	E	;compare the contents of ;acc with 5

If the accumulator contents are equal to or greater than 5 no carry will be produced and no output to the switch required. The JNC instruction can therefore be used after CMP to jump past the instructions required to operate the switch. For example:

Label	*Opcode*	*Operand*	*Comment*
	CMP	E	;compare the contents of ;the acc with 5 stored in E
	JNC	SKIP	;if acc ≠ 5 no carry ;therefore do not operate ;switch by jumping past ;instructions concerned ;with switch
	MOV	C,A	;save acc in C reg

```
        MVI     A,01H           ;load pattern to operate
                                ;switch in acc
        OUT     5               ;operate switch
                                ;device 5
SKIP:   MOV     C,A             ;continues program as in
                                ;the main example
```

Index

Accumulator, 23, 59
Address, 24
Analogue, 34
Analogue-to-digital converter
  (A/D), 34
Arithmetic and logic unit (ALU), 23
Assembly language, 18
Assembly programming, 49

Backing store, 33
Binary notation, 17
Binary representation, 17
Bit, 18
Branching instructions, 69
Byte, 18

CALL, 74
Central processing unit (CPU), 22
Comment field, 64
CMI, 93
Conversion time, 80

Data representation, 51
Data store, 16
DCR, 68
Digital-to-analogue converter
  (D/A), 34
Disk drive, 33
Display, seven-segment, 81

Erasable programmable read only
  memory (EPROM), 25

Field programmable read only
  memory (PROM), 24
Flag register, 59
Floppy disc, 33
Flow diagram, 69

Hardware, 16
Hardware fault, 46
Hexadecimal, 52
High-level language, 18, 53

IN, 72
Instructions, 16, 59
Instruction decoder, 57
Interfacing, 28
Interrupt, 38, 42
Interrupt handling, 42
INX, 68

JMP, 74
JNC, 95
JNX, 69

Keyboard, 29

Label field, 65
Low-level language, 18

Machine code, 18
Maintenance aids, 46
Memory, 16, 23
Memory mapped I/O, 74
Microprocessor, 13
Mnemonic instructions, 18, 50
MOV, 65
MVI, 65

Octal, 51
Opcode field, 64
Operand field, 65
OUT, 72

Program branch, 69
Program loop, 71
POP, 75
PUSH, 75

Random access memory (RAM), 24
Read only memory (ROM), 24
Register, 23
Register model, 23
RET, 75

Seven-segment display, 81

Software, 16
Software fault, 46
Stack, 76
Stack pointer, 58, 76
Subroutine, 74

Thermistor, 79
Transducer, 34

Visual display unit (VDU), 32

Word, 18, 22